TRACING
AN-SKY

TRACING

Jewish Collections from the State Ethnographic Museum in St Petersburg

AN-SKY

Waanders Uitgevers, Zwolle
Joods Historisch Museum, Amsterdam
State Ethnographic Museum, St Petersburg

Tracing An-sky
Jewish Collections from the State Ethnographic
Museum in St Petersburg

1992-1994
Joods Historisch Museum, Amsterdam,
Rautenstrauch-Joest-Museum, Cologne,
Jüdisches Museum, Frankfurt,
Israel Museum, Jerusalem
Jewish Museum, New York

This travelling exhibition has been supported by:

Foundation for the Jewish Historical
Museum in Amsterdam Inc., New York

With kind support of Lufthansa Cultural
Affaires

The publication of this catalogue was made
possibly by a generous donation from the
Schussheim Foundation, Haifa, Israel

We thank them for their generosity
Editor's note   7

Cover:
Folk print or 'lubok' of a Seder meal
6396-50

Page 2:
Wedding in Polonnoye

Contents

A melamed (teacher) from Podolia, 19th century

Editor's note

Because of the complex nature of the languages used in this book it proved impossible to follow any one system of transliteration. For geografical names, the spelling as given in the Times Atlas of the World was used where possible.
The article by Igor Krupnik was first published as 'Tsu der geshikhte fun etnografishe koliktsyes ' (On the history of ethnographic collections), which appeared in *Sovetish Heymland* (Moscow), no. 7, 1988, 74-81.
Mr. Krupnik kindly allowed us to print this English version, which appeared in *Soviet Jewish Affairs* vol. 19 no. 1, 1989. We have used this article without changing either the spelling of place names, names of bodies, or terminology for Judaica. These may therefore appear with a different spelling in this catalogue. Furthermore, the article has not been edited to take into account the recent political changes that have occurred in the former USSR.

The catalogue contains extracts from the memoirs of Abraham Rechtman, who took part in the expeditions organized by An-sky. The memoirs were written and published in Yiddish in 1958. The original manuscript is in the YIVO Institute in Buenos Aires; there is a copy on microfiche in Israel. We have selected interesting passages from this book and translated them, thereby adding to the 'illustrative material'. These extracts bring another facet to the exhibition.

We thank Rechtman's daughter, mrs. Faye Storch, for kindly allowing us to publish these extracts.

Sh. An-sky in 1916
photo: YIVO-Institute, New York

The Jewish Pale of settlement in Russia, 1835-1917

SWEDEN

Baltic Sea

St. Petersburg

Lake Pskov

Novgorod

Lake Ilmen

BALTIC PROVINCES

KOVNO

VITEBSK

Moscow

GERMANY

VILNA

SUWALKI

Smolensk

MOGILEV

Tula

PLOCK

LOMZA

GRODNO

MINSK

KALISZ

WARSAW

SEDLITS

Pripet Marshes

R U S S I A

Voronezh

PIOTRKOW

RADOM

CHERNIGOV

Kursk

KIELCE

LUBLIN

VOLHYNIA

AUSTRIA-HUNGARY

Kiev

KIEV

POLTAVA

Kharkov

PODOLIA

BESSARABIA

RUMANIA

EKATERINOSLAV

KHERSON

Nikolaev

T A U R I D A

Sea of Azov

KUBAN

Sebastopol

Yalta

Black Sea

TURKEY

☐ The Pale of Settlement. Russian Jews were confined to this area by laws of 1795 and 1835. By 1897 there were more than 5 million Jews in the Pale.

⊙ Towns within the Pale which were themselves barred to Jews without special residence permits.

● Towns outside the Pale with Jewish inhabitants (figures for 1897).

0   100m
0   100km

The synagogue of Shaponja

Foreword

In 1939 an exhibition was held in the then-called State Leningrad Ethnographic Museum of the Peoples of the USSR, in which some of the museum's Jewish collection was shown. It was the first and only time that these objects were exhibited. Before 1939 the First World War, the Russian Revolution and the difficult years that followed had all made it impossible to present the collection. After 1939 came the Second World War, the lack of openness of the Soviet Union and growing anti-Semitism which all contributed to the need to keep this collection as if it were non-existent.

Now in 1992, after many changes in Russia, the Jewish collection from the State Ethnographic Museum is for the first time accessible to both East and West. This exhibition and catalogue are the result of cooperation between the State Ethnographic Museum and the Jewish Historical Museum, Amsterdam. Led by the chief curator of the State Ethnographic Museum, Ludmila Uritskaya, the museum staff – under extraordinarily difficult circumstances – undertook the task of describing and restoring the entire collection. The Jewish Historical Museum of Amsterdam offered Western experience and technological know-how, when it was needed.

Above all, however, this book and this exhibition – which is planned to visit Amsterdam, Cologne, Frankfurt, Israel and New York – should be treated as a Russian presentation of objects that have been handed down to us by history. These objects witness to the lives of the millions of Jews obliged to live in the Pale of Settlement that embraced the territory between the Black Sea and Vilnius, and from Minsk to Warsaw. We appreciate tremendously the care taken by those who down the years watched over this Jewish collection through good times and bad. The exhibition is dedicated to them all – they trod in the footsteps of the collector and ethnographer, the writer Shlomo Zanvil Rapoport, known as Shlomo An-sky.

Working together can only succeed if those involved develop a sense of solidarity, of shared integrity and of personal appreciation. In a situation hampered by language barriers and cultural differences a project such as ours could only flourish with the help of an intermediary. And we found one in the person of Mrs A. Geller, of Holland-Russia Trade Services. We had the immense good luck of having her working together with us. Without her initiative, enthusiasm and enormous staying-power, we would unquestionably have become entangled in the impenetrable mazes of the changed and daily changing Russian social situation.

We thank her from the bottom of our hearts, and also for the way in which her personal involvement with this project served to bring us closer together.

There are many more who have contributed to this project, in the first place Ludmila Uritskaya, with her colleagues, and the restoration department of the museum. We also thank Igor Krupnik who generously placed at our disposal his article to be published in the catalogue. Without the untiring assistance of Marceline Dop and Lonnie Stegink of the Jewish Historical Museum, Amsterdam, who faithfully typed the endless stream of information from Russia into the database here, the catalogue would never have been completed in time.

The preparation of an exhibition and catalogue like this requires not only personal involvement but also financial support. This is the first publication of photographic material and descriptions of the collection, that had lain forgotten for decades. Our sincere thanks to The Schussheim Foundation, Haifa, Israel, for sponsoring the catalogue.

This exhibition was supported by the Dutch Ministry for Foreign Affairs, Section Cultural Cooperation and Foreign Information, KLM, the Susanna van Baerle Foundation, Venture Capital Investors, Andrea and Charles Bronfman, Canada, the Foundation for the Jewish Historical Museum in Amsterdam Inc., New York, Holland-Russia Trade Services, the Friends of the Jewish Historical Museum Foundation, Teidem BV, Leiderdorp, VSB fonds, professor Herman Musaph and Jules Markus.

We also thank Lufthansa German Airlines for their keen interest and support in the early phase of the exhibition preparation and for their generous support in the transport of the exhibition and its couriers.

All those who have made it possible to prepare and present this catalogue and exhibition deserve our deepest thanks, along with those of the entire Jewish world. Now at last the work carried out by An-sky, his predecessors and successors, is made available for research and comparison with Jewish culture as a whole. Let us hope that this book will be an encouragement and inspiration for such ventures.

Judith C.E. Belinfante
director, Jewish Historical Museum, Amsterdam

Igor Dubov
director, State Ethnographic Museum, St Petersburg

The Jewish Ethnographical Expedition

Abraham Rechtman

Abraham Rechtman during the ethnographical expedition of 1914-16 in Proskorov

Introduction

A hundred years ago Jewish ethnography was still very much in its infancy. Folklore was only just beginning to emerge as an element in Yiddish literature, while the study of the subject was limited to just a few scholars. The reasons for this are not hard to find: our grand-fathers and great-grandfathers' lifestyle was set in a particular mould. Their lives were imbued with the priceless gems of a beautiful folklore. These were handed down from one generation to the next by word of mouth and a store of legends and tales grew, full of spiritual content, poetic beauty and rich fantasy. These stories were never written down, no-one ever thought of recording their way of life, their customs and traditions for future generations. They had no reason to think that their existence would ever change; each generation succeeded the previous one, and life went on as it had always done with the synagogue and the Jewish house of study (beth hamidrash), the centres of communal life, serving and nurturing the congregation. The customs and traditions were remembered and revered; stories and legends were told and retold – respected, honoured and loved: from grandfather to father, from father to son.

The Kozin synagogue

where we came we collected the historical treasures we found: we noted down tales, legends, sayings, spells, remedies and histories told to us by men and women; we documented stories about demons, dybbuks and 'no-goods' (nisht gute), lyrics, parables, expressions and manners of speech; we recorded old melodies – niguns – on a phonograph, as well as prayers and folk songs; we photographed old synagogues, historical places, tombstones, shtiblech of tsadikim (the prayer houses of revered, pious men) and ritual scenes; and we collected or bought Jewish antiques, documents, pinkassim (record books), religious articles, jewellery, costumes and other old objects for the museum.

The synagogue of Polonnoye

But by the turn of the century many Jews had begun to abandon their traditional way of life, replacing age-old customs with totally new life-styles. They stopped telling the old stories; they started to forget their history and much threatened to become lost to posterity. It was at this time that some of our major Yiddish writers began to develop an interest in Jewish ethnography. They realised that to our generation many of the customs and traditions which had been a living part of our grandfathers' and parents' spiritual life were just remnants of the past, gradually fading in our memory – and disappearing altogether in the younger generation. They realised that there was a need to save the past while this was still possible, before all the memories and the traditions, all the knowledge of our history disappeared forever.

Jewish ethnography emerged fifty years ago as these writers began to realise the implications of what was happening. They started collecting folk-tales, stories, sayings and customs, gathering the gems of the Jewish nation's soul – their neshome – writing down and collating the oral tradition. The first Society for Jewish History and Ethnography was established in St Petersburg, and named after Baron Horace (Naphtali Hertz) Guenzburg, with a journal, the 'Perezitoe'.

One of the pioneers who dedicated his whole life to this work of preserving the Jewish heritage of past generations, was that well-loved writer, poet and collector Shlomo An-sky (Shlomo Zanvil Rapoport). An-sky organised an ethnographic expedition with colleagues including Joel Engel, a famous composer from Moscow; J. Kiselgaf, an expert on Jewish folk music from St Petersburg: Shlomo Yudovin, a painter and photographer, An-sky's cousin; J. Pikangor and S. Shrier, both students from the Jewish Academy in St Petersburg, and of course, last but hopefully not least, myself.

For three years from 1912 to 1915 An-sky led this group through God's forgotten corners of Ukraine. Every-

At the end of 1914, with the war raging, the artist S. Yudovin and myself were arrested in Zhitomir and accused of spying. Naturally, the authorities suspected us, since we went around with cameras taking pictures everywhere. So they put us under arrest and all the material we had assembled as well as the pictures were confiscated.

Meanwhile An-sky was staying in Petrograd – during the war they changed the city's name from St Petersburg to Petrograd. We sent him a telegram telling him about our situation. An-sky immediately approached L.I. Sternberg, the famous old ethnographer of the Russian Anthropologic and Ethnographic Museum of the Peter the Great Royal Academy of Sciences who managed to acquire a document saying we had been sent by the museum. As soon as Zhitomir police head-quarters received the document we were released and given back all the confiscated material. We headed straight back to Petrograd.

With that the expedition's work was officially over. However, An-sky continued to collect material. Even later, at the height of the war, travelling through Galicia as an interpreter for the War Victims' Relief Committee organized by the Duma – the Russian parliament – and dressed in military uniform with a sword at his side: even then An-sky continued his interest in ethnography and folklore. Through all the destruction of war, An-sky managed to visit devastated synagogues and religious buildings, speaking to rabbis and community leaders. From time to time he returned to Petrograd and despite this exhausting pace, he always brought boxes full of treasures and priceless historic and ethnographic material: printed decrees concerning Jews, secret decrees, documents about disputes, damaged Torah scrolls, parochets (Torah curtains) and pieces of cloth stained with Jewish blood, seals and mizrach plaques (ornamental plaque to indicate the location of the east) etc.

Once, I recall, An-sky brought a kol-bo, an all-purpose prayer-book, written on parchment, which he had found amid the ruins of a deserted beth hamidrash in a small shtetl in Galicia. From another shtetl near the front he brought pieces of parchment cut out from a Torah scroll. This shtetl was almost totally destroyed and there were no Jews left there: the synagogue lay in ashes. Looking through the remains, An-sky found a pile of broken glass and women's clothing – a testimony to the events which had taken place. Underneath all the glass, wood and clothes, he found these pieces of parchment. One of them contained the Ten Commandments, which gave him quite a shock. The parchment was torn in two: on one fragment it read: 'kill', 'adulterate', 'steal', and on the other: 'you shall not'.

In his private life An-sky was quite an unassuming and generous person. But when it came to anything connected to Jews and the honour of the Jewish people he was tough and uncompromising. Once, at a journalist club in St Petersburg a relative, also a famous journalist, approached An-sky and, putting his hand on his shoulder, he said: 'Semion Akimovitch [An-sky's Russian name], I have my residence permit for Petersburg!' But An-sky knew that you could only get a permit if you were baptised and An-sky turned round, looked him up and down, and said 'All my life I have never shaken the hand of a traitor.'

An-sky never had many personal possessions. He had no legal status all the years he had lived in St Petersburg: he had no official address there; he had no business; he wrote in restaurants and hotel rooms; he used to sleep in relatives' apartments; he had one suit and a coat. The only suitcases he had were full of ethnographic material.

After the Bolshevik Revolution An-sky returned to his literary and scientific work. He watched over the expedition and the museum's ethnographic material with eagle eyes.

Once, while staying in Moscow, he heard that the Bolsheviks had closed his museum. He returned to Petrograd immediately, broke the wax seals on the museum's locked doors and rushed over to the

A Jew from Vilna with painter's instruments, 19th century

A Jew from Vilna, 19th century

Commisariat. There he confronted the commissar and said that he was fully aware of what he had done in breaking the museum door seals, but, An-sky continued, he had been forced to do so because closing the Jewish museum was an insult to himself, the director of the institution, as well as to the entire Jewish people.

In September 1918 An-sky escaped from Russia disguised as a priest and eventually arrived in Vilna (Vilnius) a sick and broken man. He began working again, organizing a historic and ethnographic museum, the Culture League. In 1919, Vilna was swept by public disorder and a bloody pogrom in which one of the many Jewish victims was his closest friend, the writer A. Weiter. Then, under the cumulative effects of stress and pain, An-sky suffered a severe heart attack. He went to Warsaw, and on medical advice settled in Otvotzk in the forests surrounding Sosnovitch. But his health did not improve.
In a letter he wrote to me on 6 March 1920 he said:

'...I have had many adventures. For two years I wandered through Galicia; then came the first revolution! and the political situation as a member of the Petrograd Duma ..., later the second revolution and my position as a "counter-revolutionary"; September 1918 running away from Russia; with all the ethnographic material in suitcases and left in the care of the Jewish community of Moscow; the ethnographic museum in anarchy – who knows if anything still exists there; then to Vilna and the events there; the start of my heart trouble, I thought my end had come; I must give up all thought of political and social involvement.'

In another letter from Warsaw, 11 October 1920, An-sky wrote:

'I have no good news about myself. I am still ill; my feet are swollen and I cannot move around. Maybe in a couple of months I shall go to Berlin, maybe...'

But he was never to go to Berlin. He died a month after writing that letter, on 9 November 1920.

And now, almost four decades after An-sky's death and even more than four decades after the expedition through Ukraine's towns and shtetlech, nothing is left of those Jewish places. Those deep-rooted traditions of generations of Jews have now become mere memories. When I think that I am seventy and my own sun is slowly setting, I feel that as long as I breathe I must try to tell the little I remember of those few happy years I spent travelling with the expedition in the company of Shlomo Zanvil son of Aharon HaCohen Rapoport, alias S. An-sky z"l (of blessed memory).

A small apology: the material I have written here is based on a few remaining notes and pictures which I was able to keep from those times. When I escaped from Russia in 1915 via Siberia to China, and in 1916 from China via Japan to America, I was forced to leave the rich collection of pictures (1500 in all) as well as a large number of notebooks about the expedition behind. All this material remained in my home-town of Proskorov, where it was destroyed during Peltyura's pogroms. Consequently, since I have to rely solely on my memory my stories may not always be too accurate, for which I beg your indulgence.

Moreover, I have told the stories in the same way I remember them being told to me: simple, primitive and exaggerated – an integral part of the lives of those wonderful, friendly Jews, always ready to speak and tell us their stories.

My notes were written 40 years ago; some chapters have already been published in Hebrew and Yiddish newspapers and journals. Meanwhile more ethnographic material has been published about the shtetlech in Ukraine. I have therefore tried not to repeat the stories already published, unless my version is different in some way. If I have wronged anyone, I did not mean to do so and I offer my sincere apologies!

Jewish Holdings of the Leningrad Ethnographic Museum

Igor Krupnik

The State Ethnographic Museum of the Peoples of the USSR in Leningrad contains a richer Jewish ethnographic collection than any other Soviet museum. Its Jewish holdings comprise over 1,000 objects. The Museum also has a collection of hundreds of photographs and a variety of written records and postcards as well as pictures by Jewish artists. All of this constitutes a rare cultural treasure.

Most of the holdings are collections about Ashkenazi Jews. The collections about Georgian Jews, Mountain Jews, the Krymchaks and the Jews of Central Asia are kept separately as they belong to different sections in the Museum. Unfortunately, there is no overall catalogue-cum-guide of the Jewish holdings.

The last publication on the Museum's Jewish collections appeared almost twenty years ago. In a brief note, its authors, L. Ziazeva and B. Shangina, both employees of the Museum, mentioned the most interesting exhibits on the Ashkenazi Jews, gave a concise description of the structure of these holdings, and provided some details on their history.[1]

The manner in which the State Museum of Ethnography came to have its Jewish holdings is of considerable interest both for specialists and general readers. The holdings are linked with the names of well-known Jewish cultural figures of the first half of the twentieth century – Sh. An-sky (Shloyme Rapoport), Yeshue [Yehoshua] Pulner, Shloyme Yudovin and others. The history of the Jewish collection can be reconstructed in part on the basis of information found in old books and journals as well as lists and records preserved in the Museum. We shall now attempt a general overview, though many unresolved issues still remain.[2]

The Russian Museum

The State Ethnographic Museum of the Peoples of the USSR has existed as an independent institution since 1934. Before that it was known as the Ethnographic Division of the Russian Museum. The Ethnographic Division was formed in 1902, five years after the foundation of the Russian Museum, and since then entire collections and single exhibits have been assembled. This enabled the Russian Museum to secure rich holdings and open its ethnographic exhibition before the Revolution.

The first Jewish exhibits were donated to the Russian Museum in 1907 by Fedor Volkov, a well-known expert on the ethnography of the Ukraine. From 1904 to 1916 Volkov spent much time acquiring Ukrainian collections for the Museum; he also worked in Galicia and Bukovina, then parts of Austro-Hungary. In two 'ethnographic expeditions' to Chernovtsy in 1904 and 1906 Volkov acquired twelve Jewish objects which he presented to the Museum.

A further seventy or so exhibits arrived in the Museum in subsequent years. They were collected by three employees of the Museum – A. Miller in Mohilev in 1908, Aleksandr Serzhputovsky in the town of Lowicz (Warsaw province) in 1909, and A. Yakimov in the village of Shkomishche (Mohilev province) in 1910. Serzhputovsky is known primarily as an expert on the ethnography of Ukrainians and Byelorussians; Miller was a Caucasus specialist who, also in 1908, brought rich ethnographic collections from Daghestan and Azerbaydzhan, including objects obtained from the Mountain Jews of Derbent and Kuba.

Around 1914 the Ethnographic Division of the Russian Museum held 2,700 collections amounting to 140,000 individual objects. The Jewish holdings, to which individual acquisitions and gifts had been added in

F. Volkov, 1847-1918

A.A. Miller, 1875-1937

I.M. Pulner, 1900-1942

S.B. Yudovin, 1894-1954

Houses and shops in Mizjanov, 1927

1911-14, occupied a rather modest place. Nevertheless, the Jewish exhibits were displayed in the Museum's first permanent exhibition. For instance, the guide of the Ethnographic Division, which was published in 1923 and which describes the structure of the exhibition as it was after the Revolution, states that the Jewish exhibits were displayed in hall 7 together with materials on the Byelorussians, Latvians and Lithuanians, and in hall 14 together with materials on the peoples of North Caucasus and Daghestan. The exposition on the Ashkenazis comprised, the guide says, '... mostly objects pertaining to cult and manners, while materials relating to everyday life are still few.' The culture of the Jewish communities in the Caucasus was represented by 'women's attire from Derbent, Kuba and Akhaltsikh as well as embroidery and cult objects.'[3]

Nonetheless, the Russian Museum may be assumed to have been in possession by that time of two very rich collections which later became the foundation of the Jewish holdings in the State Ethnographic Museum. The two – No. 5943 comprising 125 objects and No. 6396 comprising 170 objects – are now listed in the same way: 'From S.A. Rapoport's (An-sky) collection, transferred to the Ethnographic Division of the State Russian Museum. Western Ukraine, Jews.' They were catalogued in June 1926; Pulner, at that time a university student but later manager of the Museum's Jewish section received and made a description of these collections.

The Sh. An-sky expedition

Two particulars concerning the above descriptions are of special significance. First, Sh. Rapoport (An-sky), the Jewish writer, poet, public figure and leader of the ethnographic expedition organized in 1911-14 by the Jewish Historical and Ethnographic Society in St. Petersburg, was no longer alive in 1926. He had died in 1920 in Warsaw and bequeathed the collections to this Society, which was not functioning at the time of his death. Secondly, the Society resumed its activities in 1923 and opened its own Jewish Ethnographic Museum in Leningrad on the 5th line of Vasilevsky Island, house no. 50. Out of about 1,000 exhibits in this museum 686 were from the collections An-sky had acquired in the provinces of Kiev and Podolia during his expedition.[4] Thus the Jewish Historical and Ethnographic Society was not only the official heir and owner of An-sky's collections but at that time had the opportunity to exhibit them in its museum.

To explain this matter we must go back fifteen years to the moment when the Jewish Historical and Ethnographic Society, which had been active in St. Petersburg since 1908, began a special ethnographic expedition. The expedition was named after Horace Günzburg, the Jewish community leader, banker and philanthropist whose family funded the research and regarded itself as the nominal proprietor of all the materials gathered by the expedition. In two-and-a-half years, from 1912 to the summer of 1914, the expedition's participants visited seventy Jewish shtetls in three Ukrainian provinces. An-sky was throughout its leader and the inspiration of all the research; among those who participated in the work were the specialists on Jewish folk-music and folklore Yuly Engel, Zusnan Kiselhof and the [expedition's] secretary Shloyme Yudovin, who later became a well-known artist.

Before the expedition, An-sky began, under the direction of the well-known ethnographer Leyb Shternberg, to prepare an extensive programme of 2,000 questions on various aspects of Jewish communal life, as well as their everyday life, beliefs and customs. Two hundred copies in Yiddish of this programme, which was entitled *Der Mentsh* (Man), were produced for distribution in the Pale of Settlement by members of the Society. One copy of An-sky's programme is preserved in the State Ethnographic Museum.

The results of the expedition's work is a very rich collection of ethnographic exhibits and documentary sources. According to An-sky's own account, it comprised: over 700 everyday objects, old domestic utensils, jewellery and clothing; over 2,000 photographs of scenes from everyday life, of inhabitants of the Jewish *shtetls*, and of historical and architectural monuments, cemeteries and synagogues; 500 phonographic cylinders and notes of over 1,000 folksongs and holiday and religious melodies; over 1,800 folk stories, legends and proverbs and about 1,500 texts of folksongs and folk-plays on religious subjects; a substantial number of old manuscripts, archival documents, old religious books, and numerous albums containing sketches of everyday Jewish life and Jewish types from the three provinces explored by the expedition. In addition, An-sky himself gathered a wide assortment of ethnographic and folklore material – descriptions of customs, notes he took on folk beliefs, spells, sayings and idioms – altogether 17 notebooks, diaries and separate manuscripts.

On 19 March 1914 An-sky delivered a preliminary report on the results of the expedition to a meeting of the Jewish Historical and Ethnographical Society in St. Petersburg. Several months later the First World War broke out and at the end of the summer of 1914 the expedition's workers found themselves in the front-line area in the western provinces of the Ukraine. They were compelled to stop collecting ethnographic material and all of them led by An-sky joined in rescuing Jewish cultural possessions and assisting Jewish refugees the Tsarist authorities had deported to the central regions of Russia.

A great effort was made to bring most of the materials collected to Petrograd in late 1916 but some of them remained in Moscow and Kiev. At that time the Günzburg family handed over all the materials collected by the expedition to the Jewish Historical and Ethnographic Society and renounced its rights to them with the proviso that the Society arrange for the safe-keeping, scholarly analysis and publication of all the collections and materials at the end of the war. This enabled the Society to open in late 1916 the Jewish Ethnographic Museum which held some of the materials collected by An-sky as well as earlier acquisitions. As mentioned above, the premises of the Society were located in house no. 50 on the 5th line of Vasilevsky Island. This four-storey building, erected at the expense of M. Ginsburg, a member of the Petersburg Community Board, was used for many communal purposes. On its premises were the Jewish Old People's Home, the Jewish Society for the Support of the Arts, the Orientalist courses, and the Jewish Historical and Ethnographic Society with its meeting halls, archive and museum. The Museum was open for less than a year. In the turbulent autumn of 1917 the Society closed it down and placed it in a state of conservation. It was reopened when the Society revived its activities in 1923.

An-sky himself made an evaluation of the objects he collected in a letter to the editor of the journal *Evreyskaya starina*. He wrote the letter from the frontline zone in Galicia, where he stayed in 1915 as plenipotentiary of a committee of State Duma members for helping sick and wounded soldiers and civilians who had suffered as a result of hostilities:

… The expedition purchased for about 6,000 roubles and received as a gift for an ethnic museum over 700 items, almost all of them old objects made of silver, copper, wood, etc., objects of religious observance (about 80 spice boxes, the same number of Chanuka lamps, candelabras, chandeliers, curtains, Tora embellishments, etc.), domestic utensils, women's jewellery, antique clothing, engravings, paintings … Recently I myself made a substantial collection of Jewish museum objects, documents and relics related to the present war.[5]

We do not know how or in which order all these items came to St. Petersburg. But from An-sky's published will (he died in Warsaw on 8 November 1920) we learn that apparently in 1916 or 1917 he gave for safekeeping five boxes and suitcases containing museum objects to the Ethnographic Division of the Russian Museum.[6] It would seem that the Jewish Ethnographic Society did not claim them when it re-opened its museum on Vasilevsky Island in 1923 but that they lay in the depositories of the Russian Museum without any work being done on them until 1926. They were catalogued by Pulner, who was then a student, with the assistance of A. Bril, and not by the regular staff member A. Zarembsky, who entered the descriptions of all other Jewish exhibits which arrived in the Museum in the 1920s.

It is also possible that one of the two An-sky collections in the State Ethnographic Museum is mixed and includes some objects of later provenance acquired when the Museum of the Jewish Historical and Ethnographic Society was closed down in 1929-30. An interesting inscription on an item in this collection supports this idea: 'A parchment prayerbook … donated by Sh. An-sky to the Museum of the Jewish Historical

Shtetl life

[i.e. Historical and Ethnographic – I.K.] Society in
Leningrad in 1914.'

Holdings acquired by Pulner

The subsequent fate of the holdings of the Jewish
Museum on Vasilevsky Island, which was closed down
in 1929, is not fully known. Originally the intention was
to hand over its entire holdings to the Ethnographic
Division of the Russian Museum. But they are not there
and there are no documents attesting to their arrival.
Almost all accretions to the Jewish holdings of the State
Ethnographic Museum in 1930-7 were collected by
Pulner, who in those years headed the Jewish section
in the Saltykov-Shchedrin State Public Library. The
history of the acquisition of these collections in various
regions of the Ukraine and Byelorussia as well as the
Jewish Autonomous Region is reflected in detail in
many documents – political and legal documents, report
notes, reports and letters which were left by Pulner and
are now preserved in the State Ethnographic Museum
in his personal archive and in the archive of the former
Jewish section of the Museum.

Another version of the fate of the holdings of the
museum of the Leningrad Jewish Historical and
Ethnographic Society is also linked to the State
Ethnographic Museum. It may be surmised that, after
the museum was closed, all its collections and the

archive of the Society were transferred to the Mendele
Moykher-Sforim Museum of Jewish Proletarian Culture
in Odessa. Some of the exhibits were retrieved by Pulner
for the State Ethnographic Museum in the late 1930s
and the rest were lost during the Romanian occupation
of Odessa in 1941-4, when the building housing the
Mendele Museum was destroyed.

The list of the Jewish holdings of the State Ethnographic
Museum confirms this version, at least to some extent.
For instance, two collections of forty items are described
as follows: 'From the holdings of the museum of Jewish
culture in Odessa, transferred to the State Ethnographic
Museum in 1938. Jews, Ukraine. Catalogued by
Y. Pulner and A. Bril. 15.06.1941.' It should be noted
that this was one week before the outbreak of war.
Another section of the materials Pulner brought from
Odessa has been preserved among the manuscript
holdings of the former Jewish section of the State
Ethnographic Museum. The inventory of these
documents, which was compiled in 1953, lists divorce
certificates, private letters, interventions with regard to
the provision of *matzo* to Jewish soldiers and prisoners,
Atonement Day reminder notes for the rebbe *(khsime
tsetlen)* and invitations. The first four entries on this list
are a 1911 divorce letter in Aramaic and three undated
printed wedding invitations. All four records bear the
same annotation: 'Arrived from the Museum of Jewish
Culture in Odessa in 1938.'

A report Pulner made about his business trip to Odessa
can be found in the office of the director of the State
Ethnographic Museum.

Pulner moved to the Museum to head the Jewish section

in the Ukrainian division in autumn 1937. In May-June 1938 he went on a long trip to Moscow, Kiev, Odessa, Tbilisi and Baku. His aim was to acquaint himself with the work of the Jewish ethnographic museums in Odessa and Tbilisi and the special Jewish divisions which existed at that time and to acquire new items for the State Ethnographic Museum.

Pulner's arrival in Moscow coincided with the liquidation of the GEZERD*. The liquidation commission were only too pleased to give him on the spot for the State Ethnographic Museum a section of the library and archive, paintings, rolls of film and, most importantly, an enormous collection of photographs illustrating the history of settlement of the Jewish Autonomous Region and the establishment of Jewish agricultural centres in other regions. Pulner's visit to Kiev was also successful. There, with the assistance of Moyshe Beregovsky, the head of the musical folklore section of the Jewish Cabinet of the Ukrainian Academy of Sciences, he acquired a full set

of instruments of a Jewish folk-band from the local musician (klezmer) Rabinovich – violins, clarinet, flute, drums, cymbals and trombone (twelve pieces in all). Pulner's visit to Odessa was far less successful. In his own words, he found the Mendele Museum of Jewish Culture 'in a pathetic state due to wrecking by officials of the city soviet, city (Party) committee and committee for public education.' Pulner seems not to have managed to establish a good understanding with employees of the museum and he acquired no more than a small amount of exhibits and documents. Of these the most valuable were several spice boxes, Chanuka lamps, candlesticks, ritual dishes and a set of wooden cake receptacles. A major preoccupation of Pulner in Odessa was the study of *purim-shpils*, in which he had considerable assistance from Zalman Shneyer-Okun, an employee of the Museum. A description of puppets used in *purim-shpils*, costumes for the actors and many details of the staging were reconstructed with the latter's help.

What Pulner did cannot justifiably be regarded as a purposeful attempt to return the Jewish collections in Odessa to Leningrad. The items he brought, even if

Purimshpil

they came from the holdings of the Museum of the former Jewish Historical and Ethnographic Society, could not be more than an insignificant part of those holdings. All things considered, by no means all the materials of the museum on Vasilevsky Island following its closure could have gone to Odessa.

Other materials of the Sh. An-sky expedition

This is clear from the fact that a year after Pulner's visit to Odessa the State Ethnographic Museum obtained three collections of about 150 items from the artist Sh. Yudovin, a participant in the ethnographic expedition in 1912, and from An-sky's nephew. One of the collections, which includes forty-eight drawings of patterns of Jewish ornaments, is dated 1914 and clearly belongs to the period when Yudovin participated in the expedition. For instance, it includes drawings of an ornament from a page of the book of records of the Jewish community in the *shtetl* Lyubar. It is difficult to establish whether these pictures were included in the general collection – the drawings of the ornaments are not mentioned in the short notes about the materials gathered by the expedition. There is, however, a reference to them in the first report about the opening of the museum on Vasilevsky Island in 1923.

It cannot be excluded that some items from An-sky's collections became part of other collections of the Jewish section of the State Ethnographic Museum. This is particularly evident with respect to collection No. 6802 of 87 items; unlike all other collections there is no information on when and where the items were acquired or the identity of the collector or of the person(s) who catalogued it. It comprises many old items – candlesticks, spice boxes, silver dishes, phylacteries, Tora scrolls, towels with embroidered inscriptions (e.g. 'presented to the Tsar-Emperor Nikolay II by the Jews of [such-and-such] town'). There are also engravings and drawings by Sh. Yudovin and several items which clearly belong to the 1929s-30s, for instance, the GEZERD banner.

According to G.N. Komleva, an employee of the State Ethnographic Museum, this collection was put together in 1954 when scattered museum items were dealt with. The disorder resulted from wartime, when the Museum building was severely damaged and tens of thousands of items from the permanent exhibits fund were destroyed when the storage rooms were hit by a demolition bomb.[7] Komleva recalled that several of the items which comprised the 1954 collection retained their old inventory numbers and the inscription 'From the collections of S. Rapoport'.

Thus some of the objects assembled by An-sky's ethnographic expedition or forming part of the holdings of the Jewish museum on Vasilevsky Island turned up in the State Ethnographic Museum in a manner which cannot yet be accounted for – apparently through Yudovin's endeavours. In fact, Yudovin was the true guardian of the Historical and Ethnographic Society museum. According to the Leningrad artists

Set of wooden chessmen with various Jewish attributes
6402-1/1-32

Sh. Gershov and D. Goberrnan, Yudovin lived on the museum's premises in house no. 50 in one of the rooms where the museum's holdings were stored in 1929-31, the period when the museum was shut down. In any case, we owe a debt of gratitude to Yudovin, since it was thanks to him that many of the materials which remained from An-sky's expedition were preserved and are now accessible to researchers.

It cannot be excluded that important discoveries are still to come. Under the entry 'Museums' in the *Encyclopaedia Judaica* (Jerusalem 1972, vol. 12, 540) we find, for instance, that 'A part of the Jewish Ethnographic Museum collection, especially manuscripts and ancient books, was transferred to the State Saltykov-Shchedrin Public Library in Leningrad.' This seems quite possible. But according to the *Encyclopaedia Judaica* a part of the manuscripts and printed material holdings of the Mendele Museum in Odessa was also tranferred to this library. And finally, the most intriguing fact: 'The Nazis plundered part of the collection remaining in Odessa, removing it to Germany. British forces later found it hidden in Bavaria.'[8] Who knows, maybe one day we will be able to follow up their subsequent fate.

Following the closure of theJewish Museum on Vasilevsky Island items from An-sky's collections were exhibited in Leningrad only once. This was on the occasion of the large thematic exhibition 'Jews in Tsarist Russia and the USSR' which was prepared in the State Ethnographic Museum in 1939 by a group headed by Pulner. The group included Museum staff members M. Shakhnovich and M. Gitlits and several artists, among them G. Traugot, who was responsible for the general display, A. Alekseev, V. Aronovich, N. Astafiev, V. Bashansky, V. Valyuk, S. Dergachenko, I. Dorer, B. Zhuravlev, E. Zaborovsky, T. Kaplan, Ya. Shur and Sh. Yudovin. The brief guide to the exhibition was preserved as well as a considerable amount of documents, including an itemized inventory of the material on the stands and in the display cabinets with all the inscriptions, themes and a list of sources. The exhibits occupied fifty-seven stands and were grouped in two main divisions – pre-revolutionary and Soviet. Many of the stands in the pre-revolutionary division had fairly characteristic names: 'The Jewish *shtetl* at the end of the nineteenth beginning of the twentieth centuries', 'The alliance of the bourgeoisie and Tsardom', 'The Jewish religion in the service of the Tsar and the bourgeoisie', 'On the path to October', 'The folktheatre Purim-shpil', 'The klezmer – folk musicians', 'The Jewish folk ornament', 'Jewish folk prints (luboks)' and others. Twenty-one items were exhibited in two cabinets of 'Folk art objects made of wood and metal': beakers, candlesticks, plates and dishes, boxes and a chess set (it was probably a photograph of this set that was reproduced in the 1969 article by Ziazeva and Shangina). Most of the items were undoubtedly from the collections made by An-sky's expedition.

The Soviet division of the exhibition was devoted mainly to the Jewish Autonomous Region (with such stands as 'The young town of Birobidzhan', 'Born in the tayga', 'Happy youth', 'Industrial Birobidzhan surges', 'Cultural life in the Jewish Autonomous Region', etc.). There were stands in this division devoted to the Central Asian, Georgian and Mountain Jews but these were composed mainly of photographs and pictures on the successes of collectivization in the 1930s. Finally, two stands, 'Fascism is war and hunger' and 'Fascism is cannibalism', warned of the dangers to humanity in general and the Jews in particular of fascism. Alas, who

A Jew, 65 years old, from Berdichev, 19th century

could have imagined that only a short time remained before Baby Yar, Auschwitz, the Warsaw Ghetto and Terezin!

Post-World War II additions

The German bombs which struck the State Ethnographic Museum building in 1941 destroyed a part of the valuable ethnographic collections. On 12 January 1942 Pulner, the head of the Jewish section of the Museum, died of starvation in besieged Leningrad.[9] After his death the section did not resume its activities and Jewish materials ceased to be collected. All additions to the Jewish holdings of the Museum in the post-war period are incidental gifts by people devoted to Jewish antiquities or their relatives. Currently there is not a single Jewish item on display in the Museum. Nevertheless, there is a little known page in the post-war history of the Jewish collections of the State Ethnographic Museum. In 1948 the considerable ethnographic holdings of the former Museum of the Peoples of the USSR in Moscow were transferred to the State Ethnographic Museum. The Moscow museum was created in 1924 as a result of a merger of the exhibits of the All-Russian Agricultural Exhibition with the collections of the Rumyantsev Ethnographic Museum and the Dashkov Ethnographic Museum. It functioned in the 1920s-30s, originally as the Central State Museum of Ethnology (narodovedenie).

The history of the Dashkov Museum is remarkable in itself. It was established on the basis of the exhibits of the All-Russian Ethnographic Exhibition, which was organized in Moscow in 1867 by the Society of Devotees of Natural Sciences, Anthropology and Ethnography of Moscow University. The aim of the exhibition was to demonstrate the heterogenous character of the cultures and customs of the peoples who inhabited the Russian Empire and several other, mainly Slavic, countries. For this purpose 288 dummies were made for the exhibition of representatives of various peoples in their national costumes. A sizeable number of domestic objects, tools, maquettes of dwellings, drawings and photographs were also exhibited.

Jewish items also were exhibited, including 4 dummies of Jews from the western provinces in national garb as well as 4 complete sets of Jewish clothes of 10-12 pieces each. Everyday Jewish objects too were presented – items made out of birch bark, 3 wall candlesticks and a mezuza from Mohilev; 7 items from Berdichev – candlesticks, a plate, a saucedish and a Tanakh (Old Testament) in a bag. Finally there were 39 pictures of 'Jewish national types', including rare photographs of 'Armenian' and 'Crimean' Jews.[10]

The exhibition collections were transferred to the Dashkov Ethnographic Museum, which was named after the then director of both the Moscow Public Museum and the Rumyantsev Museum, who agreed to cover most of the expenses of the exhibition. The Dashkov Museum became an important centre of ethnography: in 1905 it contained over 12,000 objects and 359 dummies. There is a detailed description of the ethnographic collections of this museum, including the Jewish ones, and its contents are well known.[11] According to the guide, there were on display in 1905 3 dummies of Ashkenazi Jews in national garb and a complete set of clothing of a Jewish woman from the province of Mohilev, 18 different objects, a model of a wooden Jewish house in the province of Mohilev, and a dummy of a Central Asian Jew in national costume.[12] After the Revolution the entire holdings of the Dashkov Museum were handed over to the Museum of Ethnology, later the Museum of the Peoples of the USSR. This new museum engaged in propaganda and academic research and also energetically gathered new materials. Its Jewish holdings too were complemented. In 1929-30 a large collection made by its staff member M. Plisetsky among the Georgian Jews of Oni and Kutaisi[13] reached the Museum. At the Museum's behest, Pulner undertook a special expedition to Byelorussia and returned with an abundance of ethnographic materials. In the 1930s, however, the Museum of the Peoples of the USSR began to reorient itself towards present-day themes and even to unload 'superfluous' materials by transferring part of its collections to other museums.

In one way or other most of the holdings of the Museum of the Peoples of the USSR reached the State Ethnographic Museum in 1948 and they remain there to this day. The Jewish holdings of the former Museum of the Peoples of the USSR are also there. But they are separate from the main body of holdings because they have a different system of listing and description. It is unclear what became of the dummies from the 1867 ethnographic exhibition. In any case, they are not at present in the State Ethnographic Museum.

Clearly, many problems connected with the history of the Jewish collections of the State Ethnograhic Museum still await investigation. It is abundantly clear that this is indisputably a great cultural treasure. The very rich collection of Jewish cultural objects in the Ethnographic Museum is of interest not only to specialists – historians, ethnographers, artists, those associated with the theatre and cinema, and musical and folklore ensembles; its cognitive and cultural value is great for millions of people of all professions. The staff of the State Ethnographic Museum have done whatever they could to preserve these holdings carefully. Now the holdings must serve scholarship and the people.

Notes

* GEZERD: abbreviation of the Yiddish name of the Society for Agricultural Settlement of Jewish Toilers in the Soviet Union.

1 L. Ziazeva, B. Shangina, 'Jewish collections in the Leningrad Ethnographic Museum', *Sovetish Heymland*, no. 1, 1969, 147-8.

2 The author expresses his gratitude to staff members of the Museum, the head of the Ethnography of the Peoples of the USSR division, N.M. Kalashnikova, and the chief keeper, L.B. Uritskaya, for their assistance in collecting materials for this article.

3 *Etnografichesky otdel Russkogo muzeya* (The Ethnographic Division of the Russian Museum) (Petrograd 1923), 27, 31.

4 'Brief descriptions of the Museum of the Jewish Historical and Ethnographic Society on the 5th line of Vasilevsky Island'. See *Evreyskaya starina*, vol. 11, 1924, 396-7, and vol. 12, 1926, 406.

5 S. An-sky, 'Letter to the editor', *Evreyskaya starina*, vol. 8, 1915, no. 2, 239-40.

6 F. Shargorodskaya, 'On An-sky's legacy', *Evreyskaya starina*, vol. 11, 1924, 312.

7 T.V. Stanyukovich, *Etnograficheskaya nauka i muzei* (The Science of Ethnography and the Museums) (Leningrad 1928), 218-19.

8 *Encyclopaedia Judaica*, vol. 12 (Jerusalem 1972), 540.

9 On Pulner see 'Yeshue Pulner' in 'Materials for a lexicon of Soviet Jewish literature', *Sovetish Heymland*, no. 12, 1981 and A. Vinkovetsky, 'The life and work of an ethnographer', *Sovetish Heymland*, no. 12, 1975.

10 *Etnograficheskaya vystavka 1867 goda Imperatorskogo obshchestva lyubtteley estestvoznaniya, antropologuii etnografii* (Ethnographic Exhibition of 1867 of the Imperial Society of Devotees of Natural Sciences, Anthropology and Ethnography) (Moscow 1878), 41, 58, 62, 67.

11 V.F. Miller, *Sistematicheskoe opisanie kollektsiy Dashkovskogo etnograficheskogo muzeya*. Vyp. I (Systematic Description of the Collections of the Dashkov Ethnographic Museum. Issue l) (St. Petersburg 1887), 153-9.

12 *Putevoditel po Dashkovskomu etnograficheskomu muzeyu* (Guide to the Dashkov Ethnographic Museum) (Moscow 1905), 21, 25.

13 *Narody Kavkaza. Katalog ukazatel etnograficheskikh kollektsiy* (The Peoples of the Caucasus. Catalogue-Index of the Ethnographic Collections) (GME (State Ethnographic Museum) Leningrad 1981), 196. Photographs of some of these items appear as illustrations to M. Plisetsky's articles 'Jews in the USSR' and 'Certain customs, rituals and beliefs of Georgian Jews' in the collection *Religioznye verovaniya narodov SSSR* (The Religious Beliefs of the Peoples of the USSR) (Moscow-Leningrad 1931).

Ashkenazi Jewish collections of the State Ethnographic Museum in St Petersburg

Ludmila Uritskaya

The history of the Jewish collections in the State Ethnographic Museum in St Petersburg began more than 50 years ago. The scale of collecting and completing material related to the Jewish culture and way of life has varied greatly at different times – after all, it had to deal with no fewer that six million people who lived within the Pale of Settlement.

The first entries related to the subject date from 1904-12, when the cultural heritage of the peoples inhabiting the vast territories of the Russian Empire attracted special interest. It was a time when there were thorough studies of the way of life among national minorities, when ethnographical expeditions were undertaken, and folklore collected. The enlightened section of the Russian intelligentsia appreciated that rapid urbanization was taking place throughout the country, and feared the consequent destruction of traditional forms of folk life, including that of the Russian Jews. Among this group were F.K. Volkov, an expert in Ukrainian ethnography, A.K. Serzhputovsky, a researcher in Byelorussian ethnography, and A.A. Miller, a specialist in the peoples of the Caucasus. They made the first contributions to the Jewish collections.

The second fruitful period for the Jewish collections was during the 1930s when the Jewish section of the St Petersburg Museum was headed by I.M. Pulner. His aim was not only to expand the collection but also to form a comprehensive exhibition entitled 'The Jews in Tsarist Russia and the USSR'. This exhibition was opened in 1939 and turned out to have a rather propagandistic character, which seemed only natural in those years.

After World War II the purposeful collecting of ethnographical data relating to the Russian Jews was virtually finished. The Pale of Settlement was now past history, while the years of brutal fascist occupation of the Ukraine, Byelorussia and Lithuania destroyed vast quantities of material culture. There was also strongly anti-religious propaganda, which became the policy of the Soviet Union and destroyed the last vestiges of spiritual life – that is, the Jewish religious communities. The tsarist policy of assimilation had not managed to bring about entirely what was successfully completed by the 'international process' of 'bringing all nations and peoples together'. During the postwar years the collections were mostly augmented with gifts from other museums, as well as rare purchases and private donations. A large collection from the former Moscow Museum of the Peoples of the USSR, which was passed on to the St Petersburg Museum in 1948, should be mentioned in this respect.

The An-sky Collection

We do well to consider in detail the S.A. Rapoport (An-sky) Collection, since the present exhibition and catalogue are mostly based on objects from this collection. It is held to be the heart and golden source of the Ashkenazi collection. An-sky headed a number of ethnographical expeditions during 1911-12, which worked in the provinces of Podolia, Volhynia and Kiev. The items collected were intended for exhibition in the Jewish Museum, formed as a section of the St Petersburg Society of History and Ethnography. The *Evreyskaya Starina* (Jewish Historical Society) magazine, the publishing organ of the Society, published articles on the collecting activities of the Museum. In 1914-16 An-sky was known to be working in the front lines of Galicia, helping to evacuate historical valuables. This mission was formed by the State Duma (The Russian Parliament) and the data he collected while there were delivered to St Petersburg. In 1917-18 *Evreyskaya Starina* reported on 'Robbery and Pogroms that have been taking place since autumn 1917, which force us to close the museum and pack the exhibits into boxes to be kept in a safe place'. From the published An-sky will it is known that: '5 boxes and suitcases with exhibits were given to be kept in the Alexander III Museum'.[1]

As we now have no precise documents or lists it is quite difficult to identify whether certain An-sky exhibits date back to 1911-12, or rather to the times of his expeditions of 1914-16. Unfortunately, the documents relating to these expeditions are lost and it proves impossible to identify the geographical source of objects. Indirect indications helping to date the items can be found when deciphering the inscriptions and also in the writings of A. Rechtman. However, we can only make guesses as to the routes An-sky followed and the places where he found his exhibits.

The combination of An-sky's personality, the immense range of his activity, amazing details of his biography and decades of oblivion following his death have given rise to all sorts of subjective interpretations and even legends around his name. The mysteries surrounding the An-sky Collections forced a new generation of researchers, historians and collectors to undertake yet another attempt to trace these collections and retrace

Oldest Torah ark curtain in the collection (1751)
6396-78

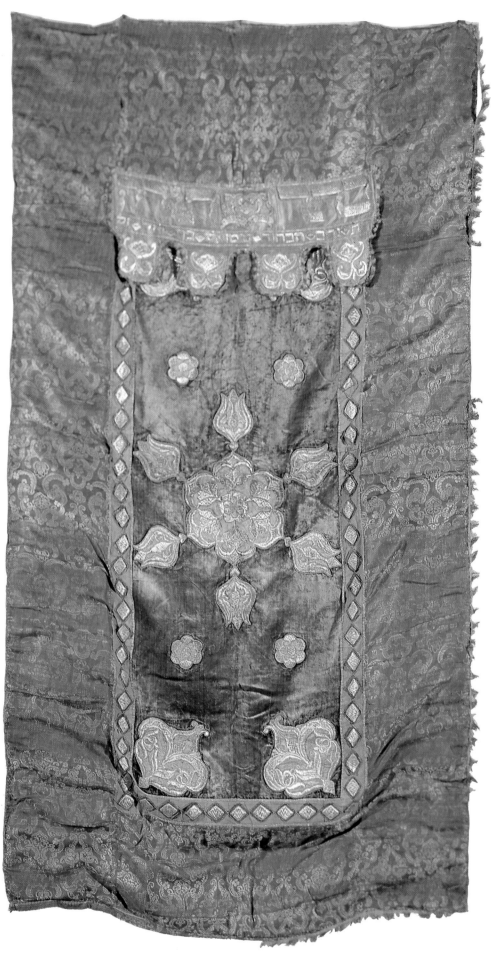

Torah ark curtain with tulips
6396-80

26

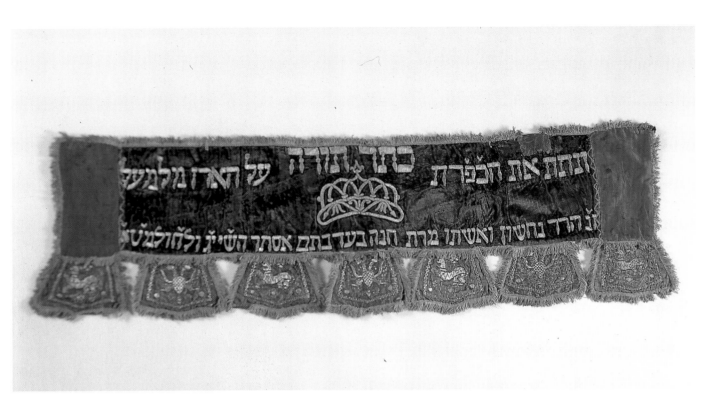

Torah ark valance (caporet) with double headed eagles and lions.
The text reads: Keter Torah (Crown of Torah)
6396-83

Torah ark valance (caporet) with double headed eagles
6396-46

Torah mantle from 1745, the oldest one in the collection
6396-84

Pair of Torah finials (rimonim) with birds on top
6802-37/38

Torah crown (Keter Torah) with a double leaded eagel on top. The
crown is shaped after an emperor's crown
6802-36

Two silver Torah shields (tas)
5943-25, 5943-28

Three silver spiceboxes (bsomim or hadas)
5943-82, 5943-106, 5943-109

Brass Chanukah lamp
5943-68, 6802-21

Chanukah lamp of zinc-coated tin-plate
4867 'D'

**China Chanukah lamp from the pottery factory in Gorodnitsa (late
19th century)**
6395-12

Kiddush cups
6802-61, 6802-59, 5943-91, 5943-88, 6802-54

34

Washbowl with inscription from Genesis (49:22). The decorations are typical folk ornaments like flowers, birds and deer
6396-5

Silver filigree mezuzah with floral decoration
5943-100

Silver phylactery cases with floral decorations and a Star of David
6802-87/1-2

**Wooden mezuzah with floral decoration and the double-headed
eagle**
6396-121

Ritual undergarment (tallit katan), made of printed calico
13134 'T'

Three 'brustichels' or bodice pieces
6396-13, 6396-33, 6396-11

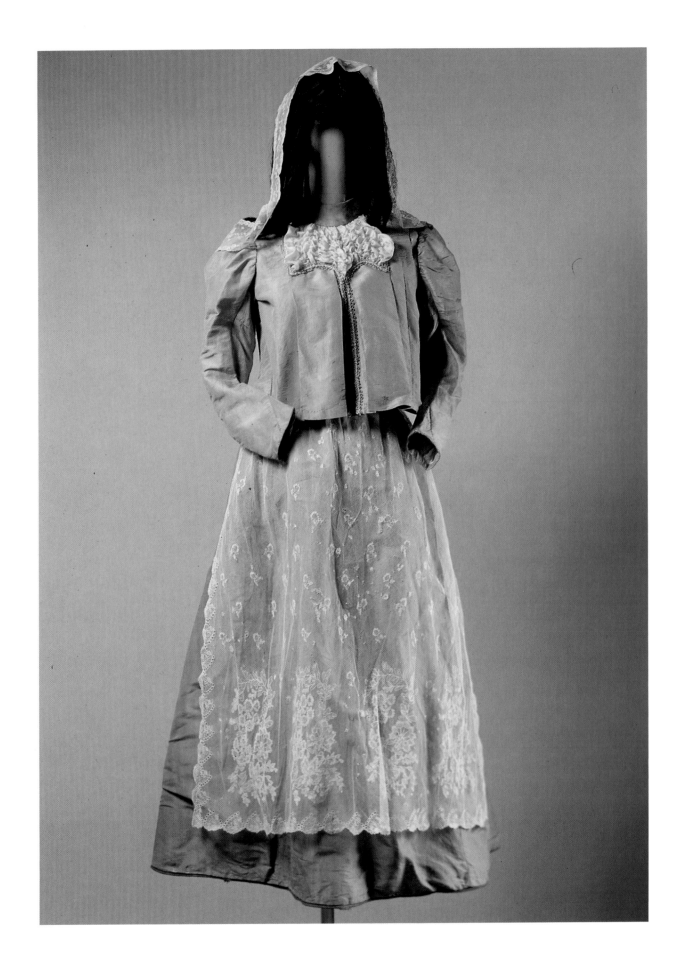

Complete women's costume with skirt, blouse, apron, kerchief and
wig
6396-58, 6396-12, 6396-66, 6396-67, 4035-4

Complete women's costume with necklace, blouse, 'brustichel',
wig, skirt and apron
13114 'T', 13090 'T', 13097 'T', 11683 'T', 6802-5, 13097 'T', 13140
'T', 13099 'T'

40

An-sky's steps. One clear result can be seen from these attempts – the preservation and thorough study of the historical and cultural heritage of Russian Jews.

What is important today is that the An-sky Collection was carefully preserved in the State Ethnographic Museum. For a number of obvious reasons, Jewish collections in the State Ethnographic Museum did not enjoy a great deal of research attention. However, the very first attempts to identify the exhibits proved extremely successful. These were deciphering of inscriptions, signatures and brand-names, contents of hand-written volumes and comparative analysis of iconographic material which open an exciting historical and cultural retrospective – in which a special place is occupied by the Jewish exhibits illuminating the civilization of eastern Europe.

Jewish Collections

The Jewish collections of the State Ethnographic Museum (Ashkenazi section) are considered to present a comprehensive historical and cultural heritage, covering the period from the late 18th to the early 20th century. In terms of geography it embraces most of the area where the Pale of Settlement was introduced after 1795 (the third partition of Poland). The Pale of Settlement included a number of provinces in the Russian Empire where Jews had the right to make their homes. The Pale included 15 Russian and 10 Polish provinces. Museum collections correspondingly represent the provinces of Volhynia, Podolia, Kiev, Poltava, Yekaterinoslav, Chernigov, Bessarabia, Minsk, Mogilev, Vitebsk, Vilna, Grodno, Warsaw, Sedletz, as well as Galicia, the Slavonic province of the Austro-Hungarian Empire.

The Judaica occupy a central place in the Museum's collection. It is organized in a manner common to any museum collection and represents a range of exhibits related to the synagogue, the annual cycle of Jewish festival, household objects, and personal belongings.

Parochets, caporets and Torah mantles

Among the items connected with the synagogue we should mention the parochets, which are splendid curtains in front of the Holy Ark, where the Torah scrolls are kept. In the Book of Exodus (26:31) we read the following: 'And thou shalt make a veil of blue, and purple and scarlet and fine twined linen of cunning work ...' The parochets are thus produced from very precious textiles, while the motifs and decorations would have biblical associations.

Four parochets or Torah curtains exhibited here date back to the 18th century. They were collected by An-sky during his expeditions to the provinces of Volhynia and Podolia. The earliest parochet (6396-78) bears the date of 1751, stated by the parochet's presenter. Both Volhynia and Podolia were parts of Poland in those days. And this is the combination of textiles, which indicates the Polish origin of this parochet, the type of textile in the central part in particular being of Polish manufacture and 18th century. The parochet is decorated with an inscription embroidered in gold and a depiction of two deer in the central part. The deer are thought to symbolise the names of the donors, Hirsh and Naftaly.

There is no reason to suppose that there were special centres of parochet production, as donations to the synagogue had a purely private character. The embroidery on the parochets was of the very highest quality. A certain division of labour can be traced here: the textile part of the parochet was usually produced by female members of the family, while embroidery could be commissioned from professional masters.

The fact that donation inscriptions and quotations were produced in imposed type-face, composed of thin silver or light brass plates, suggests that gold and silver embroidery was treated as a second phase in the production of these items.[2]

It was after the 15th century that gold and silver embroidery started developing in Europe. Baroque embroidery in Poland originated in the monastries and *szlachta* (Polish nobility) estates. Gold and silver embroidery became quite common during the 17th and 18th centuries and was used to decorate the clothes of nobility, for artistic ornamentation in the royal palaces, estates of nobility and monasteries. It acquired the status of the only fashionable and stylish decoration for all classes, including the Jewish population of Poland. Embroidery was done using a backing of cardboard, leather and pieces of cloth. Gold and silver threads were basically ordinary cotton or silk ones, entwined with thin silver and brass wires. They used silver and gilded fine spiral wire for embroidery. It was cut in short lengths and strung onto a silk thread. Embroidery patterns were cut from the cardboard and then sewn onto the textile. Applique embroidery was usually done with double gold and silver threads. Floral patterns were particularly popular, for example the tulip (6396-80), acanthus and rose leaves.

Sometimes embroidery was replaced by a woven pattern, or by lace decorations (6396-82). We cannot fail to admire one particular parochet (6396-79) produced from combined textiles. The effect is that of a combination of textiles of a similar pattern but in different colours, decorated with a small oriental pattern.

The upper part of the parochet was usually made from simple textiles and was covered with an elaborate flounce, or valance, called a caporet. The whole construction was made according to the instructions in the Book of Exodus, 25:21. Caporets were also decorated with symbolic pictures and texts. The 6396-83 caporet bears a quotation from the Book of Exodus (25:21) and a picture of Keter Torah – the Crown of Torah. Seven cones border the caporet edge with depictions of lions and double-headed eagles.

The same techniques were sometimes used in caporets as in decorations for women's clothes. For example, the 6396-77 caporet is decorated with an inset that is embroidered in the same manner as was used for women's 'brustichel' (breast decorations).

It is not difficult to deduce what social class the donor of the parochets or caporets came from: some are modest items, made from small pieces of fine textile, with various ornaments, without any embroidery; some are pretentious exhibits combining both silver and gold embroidery and enriched with monograms (6396-85).

A Torah mantle, a special cover for the Torah scroll, was one of the textile items used in the synagogue. The earliest one here dates back to 1745 (6396-84). It is decorated, according to the local Polish tradition, with golden embroidery. A later Torah mantle (1294-22) from Mogilev, Byelorussia, dates from 1870. Although this Mogilev item is related to 'classical' examples, where the effect is achieved by a combination of varying colour tones (soft blue contrasts with deep red velvet and shimmering silver and gold embroidery), nevertheless the pattern appears somewhat imperfect; this becomes clear when we look at the floral pattern that borders the edge. It betrays lack of local tradition in gold embroidery, lack of skill and competence.

Ceremonial silver objects

The majority of the silver items from the Museum's collection bears no provenance, though many of them have hallmarks which enable us to determine the exact date of production. Most of these items are from the period late 18th-mid 19th century.

The towns of Zhitomir and Berdichev were known to be the centres for silversmiths' production in Volhynia during the 18th century. Until the late 1790s they belonged to Poland.[3] These towns were also considered to be the centre of Jewish spiritual life. The largest Polish community of Jews, known as 'the Jerusalem of Volhynia' was in Berdichev. Volhynia and Podolia became strongholds of Chassidism in the 18th century. Jewish craftsmen worked side by side with Christians in small workshops in Zhitomir. Zhitomir and Berdichev silver objects were marked in Poland, Warsaw and Cracow up to the early 18th century. These objects were in demand in Odessa, Kiev, Warsaw and Vilna. Silver items were commissioned by Jews as well, mostly by the members of the religious societies of Volhynia and Podolia.

The most famous objects from Zhitomir and Berdichev show distinct traces of the Polish tradition of silver production. The shapes of cast or embossed representations of birds, animals, fruit and flowers, the engraved floral patterns combined with a number of zoomorphic motifs are clearly folklorist in origin. However, echoes of quasi Renaissance and Baroque styles are also clearly present.

The collection of silver items can be divided into several categories including decorations for the parchment Torah scrolls, Chanukah lamps, spiceboxes and other ceremonial objects.

A pair of rimonim or Torah finials (6802-37/38) from the Museum's collection has massive branches with a floral decoration engraved on it. The dedicatory inscription written on its base, stresses this object's function and purpose. It reads: 'This tree belongs to the Burial Society...' The rimonim are topped with crowns and gilded bells that announce the Torah's approach to the congregation. The tops of the crowns are ornamented with a popular decoration of birds. The same bird tops the Keter Torah – the Crown of Torah (6802-36) – shaped like an emperor's crown, decorated with superimposed silver plates forming a floral pattern. The lower edge shows Moses with the Tablets of the Law, and the Binding of Isaac.

Special Torah shields or tassim made from silver-plated copper, differ from other silver items. The tassim decoration consists of two columns, similar to 'Yakhin' and 'Boaz' – the two pillars of Solomon's Temple, or a Tree of Life – the Torah. In some tassim these columns are substituted by a floral ornament or depiction of lions or unicorns, placed in the central part, which also bears a dedicatory inscription, date or the word 'sabbath'. The majority of tassim in this collection date back to the 18th century. Their origin is not quite clear, except for the 5943-17 tas, which is known to belong to a synagogue in Nesvezh. The somewhat simple decoration of these tassim, when compared to the highly-developed tradition of lavish ornamentation, presumably indicates that they were locally produced and not commissioned from a master silversmith, whose work would be expensive.

The Jewish covenant of circumcision (Gen. 17:9-13) is also related to the synagogue. Some of the objects used during the ceremony were absolute masterpieces of workmanship. For example, the handle of a circumcision knife (6802-83) made from semi-precious stone and edged with silver. The setting is decorated with garnets and a gold alloy.

Sabbath and festivals

Following the oriental tradition, they produced vessels for aromatic spices (known as bsomim or hadas) from pure silver. The Ashkenazi collection contains such vessels of Ukrainian and Polish origin. In particular, notice here the delicately-cut filigree towers. A variety of flora is illustrated by many flower and fruit shapes. The makers of the bird-shaped vessels were possibly inspired by a popular Yiddish song, which was usually sung at the end of sabbath. This song describes the birds glorifying God. It is hard to tell whether this popular bird pattern also had a sacred meaning or was simply a detail taken from folk life. There is no doubt, however, that this motif was commonly used and popular among jewellers and craftsmen of eastern Europe.

In the Chanukiah, or Chanukah lamp, we find a rich

variety of Jewish traditional ornamentation, artistic and technical methods, and the ability to express an idea in various materials.

Our exhibition displays many different Chanukiahs – made from filigree or embossed silver, copper, tin or china. This exhibition shows among others, 'classical' examples of Polish filigree Chanukiahs, known as 'Baal Shem Tov' (3235-6), architectural Chanukiahs from the synagogues (5943-68), and a unique bronze example which is believed to date back to the 15th century, and probably comes from Italy.

The development of a tradition in Jewish bronze casting during the 18th and 19th centuries was influenced by the traditions of the applied art of the western Ukraine. The tradition of decorating bronze Chanukiahs with rosettes, snake heads, floral and geometrical patterns, was taken from Huzul (western Ukraine) bronze casting, wood carving and embroidery. The methods used when producing eight-lamped Chanukiahs and seven-lamped menorahs, when casting, metal-turning, grinding or engraving, are similar to the ones used by Lvov masters in Galicia when producing bronze lamps. These centres of production were well known in eastern Europe.

A china Chanukiah (6395-12) was produced by a pottery factory in Gorodnitsa, in the province of Volhynia, in the late 19th century. This factory as well as other pottery plants in the Ukraine and Poland, produced a wide range of crockery for Jewish festivals. The F. Zusman pottery plant, situated in the town of Kamenny Brod, province of Volhynia, operated a mass production of Passover dishes (4895'D') in the 1880s and 90s. These dishes bore printed pictures and inscriptions indicating the particular items to be used in the Seder meal.

The Jewish religion is far more than a complex of certain rituals: rather, it is a way of life. Part of it takes place in the synagogue, where the services are held. But in Jewish life the home is of exceptional importance. Hence the special significance attached to all those objects used in the home during religious ceremonies. Their sacred meaning is established by traditional form and design.

Wine is drunk from the Kiddush cup on the sabbath and festivals to mark the holiness of the day. These cups (5943-91, 6802-61) are made from silver. In Poland and Russia crockery in the shape of small decorated cups (6802-54) was used for Kiddush, as well as silver (5943-88) and copper (5943-7) drinking vessels. Jewish craftsmen would cover the surface of this crockery with engraved ornamentation, illustrating biblical scenes (5943-90), or using sacred symbols (5843-88). A Ukrainian glass factory of the late 19th century produced festive pieces to be used at Passover (7851-11, 6407-1). Inscriptions, produced in excellent square typeface in Hebrew, proved to be the best decoration for these items.

A mezuzah protects a Jewish house and reminds everybody that a home is a sacred place. Special cases to hold a small piece of written parchment (Deut. 6:4-9, 11:13-21) were made of various materials including tin, glass and wood, as well as beautiful silver filigree (5943-100). Some of these mezuzah cases are most unusual (6396-121), having, for example, an architectural design. A certain influence from the Carpathians can be seen here in the wood carving.

There are certain items worn by male Jews as part of their religious observance. Among these are, for example, small boxes called phylacteries or tefillin, praying shawls – the tallit or talles – and arba kanfot, or tallit katan, a ritual undergarment.

Phylacteries are small boxes containing four extracts from the Bible (Ex. 13:1-10, 11-16, Deut. 6:4-9, 11:13-21). They are attached to the head and left arm with straps and were often kept in silver cases. These silver containers are in some cases remarkable works of art (6802-87/1.2).

Praying shawls, or tallit, were usually made from silk or wool, with black or blue bands woven at the edge. In Russia, tallits were made of fine white wool. The town of Dubrovna, in the Mogilev province, was the centre of this production. Mezuzahs and phylacteries were also made here.

Arba kanfot refers to a ritual undergarment worn by men. They are rectangular-shaped pieces of cloth, with no seams and with a special opening for the head, and with tzizit (fringes). This piece of decoration is distinctive for Jewish clothes. Sometimes they used tallit textiles to produce arba kanfot, or printed cotton with a simple pattern (13128'T', 13134'T'). The opening was treated as the collar of a man's shirt.

Clothing

No thorough study of Jewish clothing in Russia has so far been made. However, the rare examples we have, together with illustrative material, suggest that there were quite a few local variants of Jewish clothing in 18th- and 19th-century Russia.

Jewish costume of the 18th century generally developed from the traditional local costume with some specifically Jewish elements being added. Jewish clothing of south-west Russia was based on Polish *szlachta* (nobility) costume. Men's clothes included long flapped kaftans, silk robes, high boots, various types of fur coats, skull-caps and fox 'shtroimele' hats. Breeches, white stockings, shoes and long kaftans were typical for Chassidim. Tsadikim preferred light-coloured clothes, as they believed that these colours symbolise purity and sanctity. Women's clothing of this period shows a taste for expensive textiles and elaborate decoration. Women's clothing of Lithuanian Jews in the 18th century comprised silk skirts and blouses, usually worn under a long dark cloak with long sleeves falling at the back. Headgear consisted of a large piece of textile, folded on the head, so that three edges fall down loosely. Turban-shaped headgear was quite common both in Lithuania and in the Ukraine.

Jewish women of Galicia continued to wear skirts, blouses, aprons, kaftans, headgear of various shapes decorated with pearls, and the breast decorations known as 'brustichel' (17th-early 19th century).

Beginning in the first decade of the 19th century, Russian legislation tried to formalise Jewish clothing, and passed various laws and decrees in this connection. The aim was to abolish those elements of national costume which were considered symbolic in terms of a sense of Jewishness. Such items included beards, sidelocks, traditional male headgear, and the wigs worn by married women.

Traditional orthodox Jewish costume was seen as part of Jewishness itself, hence every deviation from the tradition was considered as deviation from the religion. For example, the tsar's decree of 1842 was regarded as disastrous, and was followed by prayers and fasting. A decree of 1851 banned Jewish married women from shaving their heads and wearing wigs. The 1851 regulations read: 'Items of Jewish clothing banned for wearing are as follows: silk and prunella robes, belts, "krymka" fur hats, and others of purely Jewish origin, with peaks, skullcaps, short trousers and boots of the same nature. Jews are not allowed to wear "peoth" [sidelocks]. Jewish women must wear either ordinary caps or ladies' hats, dresses of ordinary cut similar to the ones worn by Russian women... It is forbidden to wear ... false hair, as well as padding made of ribbons, satin, worsted yarn and suchlike as headgear. Jewish women are to be inspected to discover whether or not they are shaving their heads; examination is to take place on the premises of local authorities in the presence of her husband or immediate relative...' Local authorities often carried out these injunctions in a most indecent manner and mass complaints forced the government to reconsider these measures.

Not until the late 19th century were the decrees of the tsar revoked. Peak-caps became a common form of male headgear. With the spread of education in Jewish communities, particularly in the cities, a new style of civilian dress was adopted by both men and women, especially among the Jewish intelligentsia. However, there were three items of female clothing which proved highly resistant to change and fashion. Although altering slightly, they remained in use up to the First World War. These are: the women's bodice pieces called 'brustichels', aprons and headgear.

Three full sets of women's clothing from the late 19th century are shown in the Museum's collection. There are two dresses, composed of blouse and skirt from the provinces of Volhynia and Podolia (An-sky Collection). These costumes are made of silk, with wide gathered skirts and blouses with a concealed fastener. This fastener was usually hidden beneath the 'brustichel'. The origin of this element of Jewish female costume is still unknown. It is thought that its original function was that of magical protection, as is the case with all types of breastplates and bodice pieces among other peoples.

This garment usually consists of a vertical textile band, fixed on cardboard. 'Brustichels' were fastened with a string round the neck and the lower part was tucked into the skirt. The 'brustichels' in the collection illustrate one type of decoration: a silk or velvet band, beautified with gold and silver embroidery, as well as spangles and foil, and trimmed with so-called 'Spanish brocade'. Starting in the 18th century both Poland and Galicia had established centres of 'Spanish brocade' making. This lace was used to decorate female clothing, as well as skullcaps, tallits, parochets, caporets and collars. 'Spanish brocade' was produced in long bands and was cut according to demand. The edge or 'agreamante' was a special feature. A 'brustichel' from a Berdichev woman's costume of the 19th century is produced from the same textile as the waistcoat and has the same ornamentation, which, though simply made, still shows the influence of the tradition. Although the function of the 'brustichels' in female costume appears to be of minor importance, nevertheless the way it was worn led to a specific type of posture – hands were hidden in it in the same way as they are in a muff.

Women's waistcoats were produced from luxurious textiles and decorated with a border; tightly-rolled strips were attached to the lower edge of full skirts, to hold them out.

Originally aprons appear to have possessed the same magical role as 'brustichels'. Later, however, utilitarian and decorative functions predominated. Aprons became an integral part of the Jewish female costume. Even after they had gone out of fashion, the most conservative women would still wear aprons, hidden beneath their skirts.

Female costume was completed by knitted stockings and slipper-like shoes without backs. This type of footwear was worn until the late 19th century. Female headgear is illustrated by velvet kerchiefs decorated with golden embroidery or made of fine veil, as well as caps made from calico and silk brocade. 'Haup' or 'Houb' caps are thought to be unique. One of them (1564-7), from the town of Lovich in the province of Warsaw, is made of black lace and decorated with ribbons, pieces of velvet and lace. The other (6396-19) is circular with long silk fringes which suggest long hair. Headgear was worn in combination with wigs and kerchiefs. The oldest types of wigs were made from textile and decorated with a great variety of stitches, producing shapes like curls, and cones of various sizes. It was in the late 19th century that textile wigs were replaced by ones produced from natural or artificial hair. A variety of such wigs was able to satisfy all the different tastes. This exhibition includes a collection of wigs.

Male clothing is illustrated by shirts, kaftan-type jackets, belts and headgear.
A 'kittle' (1654-6), or prayer shirt, was worn once a year, when attending the synagogue on Yom Kippur, the Day of Atonement, and for special occasions such as weddings and funerals. This type of shirt is included in the 'takhrikhim' funeral set (1294-10).

A Jewish family. The woman is wearing a wig

Men's kaftans, produced in the late 19th century in the province of Vilna (13083'T', 13087'T', 13088'T') were made of black or dark-brown material and decorated with velvet. Although these kaftans had button-fastenings they were worn with 'gartle' belts, which had the same symbolic meaning as female aprons.

The robe which once belonged to a tsadik from Kaidanov (6396-3) is produced of light textile and has a belt. Its pockets, sleeve edges and openings, are decorated with red lace, which was believed to function as an amulet.

In the late 19th century the kaftan was replaced by a new brand of 'capote'-type clothing – a short coat trimmed with silk or velvet. 'Capote' was usually worn with 'akhyt' or 'kartuz' headgear, similar to a peak-cap. Fur 'shtroimele' were modified in terms of size and decoration: traditional fox was displaced by short-napped types of fur.

Amulets

The Jews in Russia were in an exceptional position. They had few legal, social or economic privileges. Because of this many Jews tried to invent their own means of protection and turned to mystical forces. Despite the fact that Judaism forbids the use of magic, nevertheless 'komea' (amulets) became exceptionally popular with Jews, especially in the south-west of Russia and in Poland, in the areas where Chassidism was strong. Even Lithuanian 'mitnaggedim' (opponents of Chassidism) who were commonly known for their temperance and good sense, turned – when they were totally exhausted by poverty – to the use of amulets. Jewish amulets contain a wide variety of texts written

on pieces of parchment. They were composed by people known as 'Baal Shem', special holy men who understood the mystery of God's name. The particular requirements to be met when writing an amulet were laid down in a manuscript dated 1792-95 and composed by a certain Isak, the son of Arye Leib Kats from the city of Grodno. The person who composes the text of the amulet is expected to have sufficient knowledge of angelology and demonology to know the magic of names and have some understanding of cosmic time and space. He must also know how God's names are combined. As for his spiritual background, the amulet-maker must take his task seriously, be an upright person and observe the fasts.

Various types of amulets are exhibited here. Written amulets for a woman in childbirth and her child were meant to protect them from evil and were believed to be the most effective ones. These evils were set out in symbols in the book 'Sefer Raziel'; the amulets date from the 11th century (6410-40) and were thought by some Jews to be composed by Adam himself. The 6410-38 amulet also originates from 'Sefer Raziel' and is believed to protect a woman and her child from the demon Lilith; it has the names of angels and demons written on it. The 6410-39 amulet has the same function and was for a newly-born son; it also bears a picture of a boy. This type of amulet proved exceptionally popular and we can see other similar ones dating from the 17th and 18th centuries. The only alterations they introduced were in the clothes, which inevitably changed with the passage of time, and from place to place. An amulet shown in this exhibition depicts a boy wearing the clothing and headgear typical for men living within the Pale of Settlement in the late 19th to early 20th century.

Many kinds of amulets, intended for every possible occasion, are known to exist. There are those to protect the owner from the Evil Eye, with a specific formula

Amulet to protect women in childbirth
6410-38

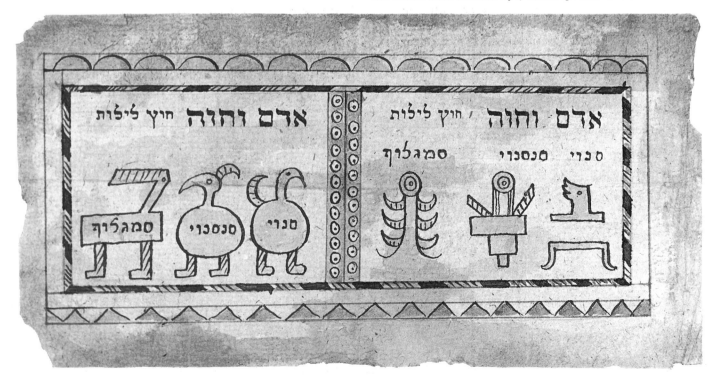

inscribed around the menorah (6369-149); the ones to protect the house and its inhabitants from the Evil Spirit (6410-41), with names of angels and demons on it; amulets to protect against fever (6395-135); ones for protection in war (6396-136), and universal amulets to protect against witchcraft, illness and so forth (6396-137).

Medicinal amulets were used by Jews in the same way as they were used by Christians. These amulets were usually composed by Jewish midwives, old, childless women, or by Christian pilgrims, Tartars or Gypsies. Medicinal amulets usually combined various herbs, roots and aromatic seeds. Those amulets which proved effective were passed down from generation to generation.

The manner of writing the text and wearing amulets varied. For instance, those amulets which were intended to attract someone's attention were written using a copper pen and rose-water. Incantations against robbery were written with a nail on wax, or with a needle on the wall. Amulets would be worn round the neck or fastened in the clothing, attached to walls or curtains, hidden in safe places, placed in small bags, walking sticks, or the heads of stamps used for sealing. Rings were also worn as amulets (5943-125, 6802-66). During the funeral of a righteous man, special messages – 'kvitlach' – asking for help and protection were placed on the grave (6396-91/1-3).

In the late 19th century gold and silver amulets, depicting Moses with the Tablets of the Law, first made their appearance (5943-59, 6802-70). They were worn round the neck in the same manner as Christians wear a cross. A metal medallion-shaped amulet for children, known as 'hejele', was specially popular. It was believed to protect babies from illness and misfortune.

Wall amulets with magical texts by anonymous authors from the 17th and 18th centuries were in particular demand. These texts were produced in Russian-Jewish publishing houses. Magical texts, combined with the Psalms and accompanied by comprehensive illustrations, were commonly recommended as amulets. Three amulets of this type are shown in this exhibition: 'Jacob's Dream' (6396-169), 'David and Bathsheba' (6396-130) and 'Isaac blessing Jacob' (6396-129). Bible subjects are presented in the manner of a cheap popular print. Sometimes the author tries to diverge from this tradition and fills the pictures with realistic details. For example, he depicts Bathsheba dressed as a 'grande dame' since he believes that this is how the tsar's wife should look. She wears her hair in an elaborate style, and has a shawl and a lace collar. David himself is wearing even more exotic dress. As for the interior, there are quantities of draperies and a violoncello rests against the wall. In the scene showing Jacob's blessing, the young Esau and Jacob are dressed in ordinary boys' clothes. However, in cases when the artist has to depict divine revelations (such as Jacob's Dream) he turns it into a symbolic piece. The landscape shown is what the painter imagined as 'biblical'.

Folk prints or 'luboks' and paper decorations

There are six Jewish folk prints or 'luboks' devoted to Hagadah and Bible subjects in the Museum's collection. 'Jacob's Funeral', 'Rebecca and Eliezer', 'Balaam and the ass', 'Lot leaving Sodom', as well as the 'Seder' scene, are all produced in a precise and simple manner. On one hand, the picture is quite conventional, but at the same time the details, including the faces of the characters which reveal their state and mood, are extremely individualised. Lot's wife and daughters are wearing clothes which are very similar to those worn by the Ukrainian Jews of the mid 19th century – turban-like headgear, dark skirt and shirt, an apron. Men from the 'Seder' scene are wearing traditional kaftans and headgear. Soldiers pictured in the scene showing Balaam and the ass are dressed in Russian military uniform of the mid 19th century.

The David and Goliath print is clearly the work of another artist. The picture is outlined with a decorative frame. David's army, the people of Israel, are wearing Chassidic dress. The Philistines and Goliath are dressed in imaginary uniform, somewhat resembling an early 19th-century French one. Probably this print dates from an even earlier period and the uniform merely echoes the 1812 war. These prints are full of both irony and inexhaustible optimism.

Paper decorations, called reyzele, can certainly be described as folklore examples of Jewish applied art. They are attached to windows and walls on the eve of Shavuot (Feast of Weeks). This tradition originates from the custom of decorating both synagogue and home with green branches, herbs and flowers during the Shavuot festival. Green symbolised the blooming hills of Sinai. The art of making paper, carved and ornamented reyzele developed from the 'mizrach', or decorated panels – produced from various materials, which judicates the East.

Reyzele were specially popular in places where a certain local tradition of this type had already existed. These were Polish, Ukrainian (western areas), Byelorussian (Volkovyss area), Lithuanian (Baslaw area) cut out decorations, made of paper, which enriched new types of reyzele.

The reyzele collection was formed by S.B. Yudovin, a famous artist, who was known to be a great expert in Jewish ornament design. A number of reyzele samples from Beskenkovichi (Byelorussia), were produced by the artist himself and based on various pieces he had collected at different periods.

Purim-shpil

S.B. Yudovin presented the Museum with a collection of sketches for costumes intended for 'Purim-shpil' performances (Purim plays), and also the props which had been produced in Beshenkovichi. The performance took place in 1932, and following the tradition, all the roles were played by men. The groups of 'Purim-shpilers' used to travel from one house to another during the Purim festival, performing plays which were based on the biblical Book of Esther. However, the story of this queen was only a framework. Much embroidery was added by the actors in the way of satire and frivolous humour, accompanied by music and dancing. Klezmers, the folk musicians, took part in 'Purim-shpils' and were invited to play at weddings and festivals. A set of musical instruments, used by klezmers, are exhibited here. This collection was donated to the Museum by Rabinovich, an old klezmer from Odessa. His touching letters are carefully preserved.

Traditional bakery

A considerable part of this exhibition is devoted to examples of traditional bakery from Bershad, in the province of Vinnitsa, Ukraine. This material proves to be exceptionally varied both in shapes and terminology. That is where we can see most clearly the interaction between Jewish, Ukrainian and Russian traditions. There is, for example, the bread (challah) for sabbath made in the shape of a bird, which is specific for Russian religious and family baking. There are also 'loiter', in the shape of a ladder, made for Yom Kippur, while in Christendom the ladder is the symbol of the Ascension. These bread rolls were baked in Russia especially for Ascension Day.
Together with traditional 'hommentash' (Haman taschen), baked for the Purim festival, they also made all kinds of pastry of various shapes – animals, human figures and ornamental forms. 'Monele' pastry, baked with poppy seeds and 'lekechl' sugar pastry, were combined with traditional Russian filled pies.

Unique photographs

A collection of unique photographs complements the exhibitions. These photos are precious documents that record the geography and way of life of the inhabitants of the former Pale of Settlement. They show the north-west and south-west areas of Russia at the end of the 19th and beginning of the 20th century. We see shtetls, synagogues, respected Talmudic scholars, Jews at prayer, wealthy members of the community, poor craftspeople, tradesfolk, lawyers, musicians, men, women and children. Together with the extremely rich ethnographical material, these photos render an inimitable image of an original, unique Jewish culture. It developed over more than two centuries in close contact with the multi-national culture of Russia. Regretfully, this Jewish culture no longer exists.

Notes

1 Presently the State Ethnographic Museum. An-sky exhibits were stored in the department of Ethnography of the former, which became an independent museum in 1934.
2 The State Ethnographic Museum possesses 116 silver letters in Hebrew, once forming the inscription on the parochet. There is a number of parochets with inscriptions made in imposed letters in the Lvov Museum of Ethnography.
3 Zhitomir became part of Russia in 1778, Berdichev in 1793. After 1843 Berdichev adjoined the province of Kiev.

Velvet cap (houb) for a woman, with silk fringe
6396-19

Coat and belt for a man
13088 'T', 13068 'T'

Silk skullcaps with Spanish brocade (shpanyer)
6396-7, 6396-43

Folk print or 'lubok' of David and Goliath
6396-48

50

Folk print or 'lubok' of David and Bathseba. This print served as an amulet
6396-130

Paper cut-out mizrach with folk decoration and blessing hands
6396-103

Front page of a pinkas from Medzhibozh
6395-14

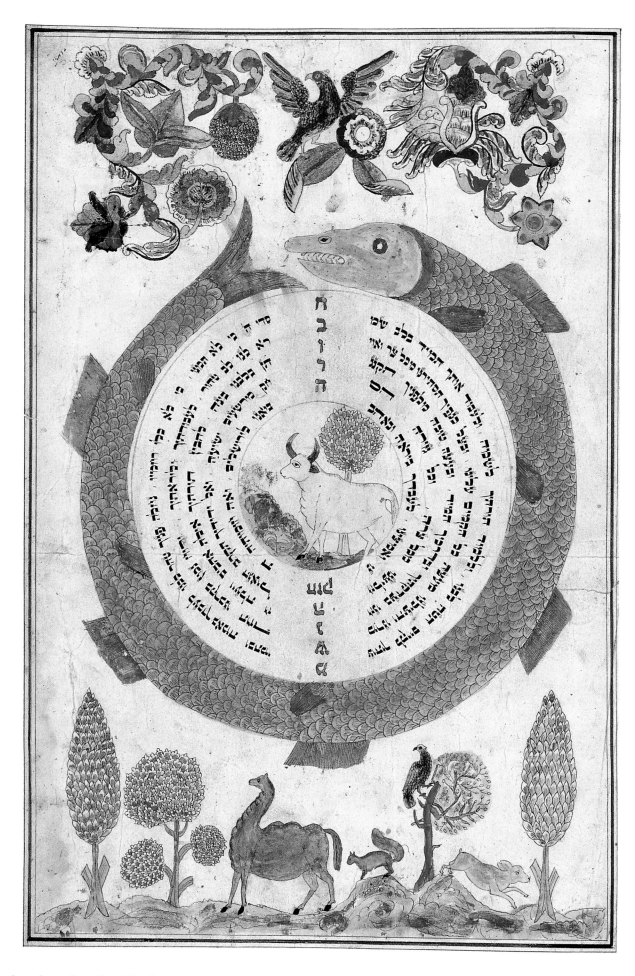

Illuminated page from the pinkas from Medzhibozh
6395-14

54

Артаксеркс

Мордехай

Two sketches by Yudovin for Purim-sphil costumes:
King Ahasveros and Mordecai
6410-2, 6410-5

**A model of a cake (kitka) and two models of a challah, made for
sabbath**
6406-4, 6406-12, 6406-14

Literature

Ludmila Uritskaya, *Ashkenazi Jewish collections of the State Ethnographic museum in St Petersburg.*

Russian

M. Berlin, *Ocherki etnografii evreyskogo narodonaseleniya* (Essays on the Ethnography of the Jewish Population), St Petersburg 1861

Etnografiya vostochnih slavyan (The Ethnography of Eastern Slavs), Moskva 1985

Evreyskaya entsziklopediya (Jewish Encyclopedia) t. I-XVI, St Petersburg

S. Dubnov, *Evrei v Rossii i Zapadnay Yevrope* (Jews in Russia and Western Europe), 1923

S. Dubnov, *Evrei v tsarstvovanii Nikolaya II* (Jews in the reign of Nicolas II), Petrograd (Kadima) 1922

O. Gantszkaya, *Narodnoye iskusstvo Polshi* (The Folk Art of Poland), Moskva 1970

Y. Gessen, *Istoriya evreev v Rossii* (History of Jews in Russia), St Petersburg 1914

'Itogi deyatelnosti EIEO' (Review on the activities of the Jewish Historical Ethnographical Society), *Evreyskaya starina*, t. X (1918)

P. Joltovski, 'Pametniki evreyskogo iskusstva' (Monuments of Jewish Art), *Dekorativnoye iskusstvo*, 9 (1966)

P. Joltovksi, *Hudojestvennoe lityo na Ukraine v XVII-XVIII* (The Art of Casting in the Ukraine in the 17th-18th century), Kiev 1973

Jivopisnaya-Rossiya (Picturesque Russia), Moskva 1890

N. Kamanin, *Evrei v Levoberejnoy Ukraine v XVII veke* (Jews of Leftbank Ukraine in the 17th century), Kiev 1891

I. Malishevskii, *Russkie izvestiya o evreyah v Kieve i Yujnoi Rossii v X-XII vv* (Russian News on Jews in Kiev and Southern Russia in the 10th-12th century), Kiev 1892

F. Petreakova, *Ukrainskii hudojestvenniy farfor. Konetsz XVIII-nachalo XX* (Ukrainian artistic porcelain. End of 18th-Beginning of 20th century), Kiev 1985

M. Plisetszki, *Evrei v SSSR. Sbornik 'Religioznye verovaniya narodov SSSR'* (Jews in the USSR), Moskva-Leningrad 1931

M. Postnikiva-Loseva, N. Platonova, E. Ulyana, *Zolotoye i serebrennoe delo XV-XX* (Golden and Silver Craft), Moskva 1983

F. Shargorodskaya, 'O nasledii An-skogo' (On An-sky's legacy), *Evreyskaya starina*, t. XI (1924)

Non-Russian

D. Altshuler (ed.), *The Precious Legacy. Judaic Treasures form the Czechoslovak State Collection*, New York 1983

Ch. Benjamin, *The Stieglitz Collection. Masterpieces of Jewish Art*, Jerusalem 1987

G. Frankel, 'Notes on the Costume of Jewish Women in Eastern Europe', *Journal of Jewish Art*, vol. 7, 1980, p. 50-57

Z. Gitelman, *A Century of Ambivalence. The Jews of Russia and the Soviet Union, 1881 to the present*, London 1988

J. Gutman, *The Jewish Sanctuary*, Iconography of religions, vol. XXIII,1, Leiden 1983

J. Gutman, *The Jewish Life Cycle*, Iconography of religions, vol. XXIII,4, Leiden 1987

Judaica. Catalogue of the Exhibition from the Museum of Historic Treasures in Kiev. Turku (Finland) 1991

B. Kirschenblatt-Gimblett, C. Grossman, *Fabric of Jewish Life: textiles from the Jewish Collection* , vol. I, New York, The Jewish Museum 1977

H. Lileyko, *Zlotnictwo*, Warszawa 1978

A. Rubens, *A History of Jewish Costume*, London 1973

L. Shachar, *The Jewish Year*, Iconography of religions, vol. XXIII,3, Leiden 1975

Tardy, *Les poinçons de garantie internationaux pour l'argent*, Paris 1987

J. Ungerleider-Mayerson, *Jewish Folk Art: from Biblical Days to Modern Times*, New York 1986

Catalogue

The catalogue is arranged in accordance with the collection in which the object is found in the State Ethnographic Museum of St Petersburg. The collections follow each other in chronological order. Within each collection the ordering is numerical, according to the inventory number.

Information about each object is presented in the following manner: inventory number, name of object, short decription including any inscriptions on the object, the name of the maker (when known), materials used, silver marks (if present), measurements, place and year of production, and finally the place where the object was found. The reference *Tardy (1987)* comes from the literature list made by Ludmilla Uritskaya. At the back of the catalogue is an alphabetical index listing the names of the objects.

Extracts from Abraham Rechtmans's book are used as complementary material.

F.K. Volkov Collection, 1904/1906

854-1
Man's fur hat
Known in Yiddish as a streimel, from the Polish 'strj' (costume), this is a characteristic Jewish hat worn on the sabbath in Galicia in the 18th-19th century.
Velvet, polecat tails, oil-skin, 21 cm (diam.) x 20 cm
Austria-Hungary, Bukovina, Chernovtsy, 1880-1906
from: Bukovina, Chernovtsy

854-5/a,b,c
Tefillin
Phylacteries, or tefillin, together with a black velvet bag in which they were usually kept (called in Yiddish: tefillin-zekle).
Leather, paper, parchment, 4 x 5.5 x 4.5 cm
Austria-Hungary, Bukovina, Chernovtsy, 1880-1906
from: Bukovina, Chernovtsy

854-10
Menorah
The lamp is supported by a massive stem with circular base and moulded decorated brackets. The combination of turning and moulding was characteristic for the design of small lamps, manufactured in the workshops of Lvov (Lemberg) in the 18th century.
Brass, 36.5 x 47.5 cm
Poland, 1700-1800
from: Austria, Bukovina, Chernovtsy

A.A. Miller Collection, 1908/1911

1294-2
Rabbi's hat
Velvet hat trimmed with fur (Yiddish: ahit). This type of man's hat was introduced into Jewish costume as a result of tsarist edicts of 1840 and 1850, forbidding Jews to wear different clothes from the Gentile population of Russia. Velvet caps with lacquered peaks were popular among the raznochin population of Russia of the second half of the 19th to early 20th century.
Velvet, kidskin, 20 cm (diam.) x 10 cm
Byelorussia, Mogilev-on-Dnjepr, 1880-1908
from: Byelorussia, Mogilev-on-Dnjepr

1294-3
Skullcap
A skullcap for everyday use. This one has six gores sewn together, with a flat black button at the top.
Velvet, kidskin, 16 cm (diam.) x 10 cm
Byelorussia, Mogilev-on-Dnjepr, 1880-1908
from: Byelorussia, Mogilev-on-Dnjepr

1294-4
Skullcap
A skullcap (Yiddish: yarmulke) for festivals. Made of dark blue silk, with silver embroidery - so-called Spanish brocade (Yiddish: shpanyer).
Silk, metal thread, 17 cm (diam.) x 13 cm
Byelorussia, Mogilev-on-Dnjepr, 1880-1908
from: Byelorussia, Mogilev-on-Dnjepr

1294-5
Skullcap for Yom Kippur
A skullcap made of ornamented silk. Decorated with a floral pattern and trimmed with Spanish brocade (Yiddish: shpanyer).
Silk, metallic ribbon, cotton, 18 cm (diam.) x 14 cm
Byelorussia, Mogilev-on-Dnjepr, 1880-1908
from: Byelorussia, Mogilev-on-Dnjepr

1294-6
Skullcap for Yom Kippur
A brocade skullcap (Western Europe, 18th to 19th century), with silk-embroidered roses, trimmed with silver braid.
Brocade, metal thread, spangles, cotton, 19 cm diam. x 15 cm
Byelorussia, Mogilev-on-Dnjepr, 1700-1900
from: Byelorussia, Mogilev-on-Dnjepr

1294-7
Decoration on prayer shawl
This decorative neck-piece, made of openwork brocade (Yiddish: shpanyer), is sewn onto strips of silk textile.
Silk, metal thread, 78 x 12 cm
Byelorussia, Mogilev-on-Dnjepr, 1700-1900
from: Byelorussia, Mogilev-on-Dnjepr

1294-8
Tallit katan
A small tunic with black stripes, with an opening for the head. The collar is fastened with two buttons. Tzitzit (fringes) are attached to each corner. This ritual undergarment is worn by boys from early childhood onwards.
Produced in a workshop in the province of Mogilev
Wool, cotton, 72 x 55 cm (unfolded)
Dubrovna, 1900-1908
from: Byelorussia, Mogilev-on-Dnjepr

1294-10 a,b,c,d,e,f,g
Burial clothes
A complete set of white cotton garments for dressing the dead (Yiddish: takrihim).
a. shirt (Yiddish: gemd): 98 cm
b. trousers (Yiddish: geizom): 107 cm
c. shirt-cover (Yiddish: kittle): 105 cm
d. belt (Yiddish: gartle): 120 x 30 cm
e. skullcap (Yiddish: yarmulka): 28 x 30 cm
f. small bag for earth (Yiddish: yard kissen): 17 x 17 cm
g. shroud (Yiddish: lalach) : 154 x 157 cm
Cotton
Byelorussia, Mogilev-on-Dnjepr, 1900-1908
from: Byelorussia, Mogilev-on-Dnjepr

A Byelorussian Jew, wearing a tallit katan, 19th century

1294-12/1-2
Child's tefillin
Phylacteries, used by children.
Leather, paper, parchment, 3 x 4.5 x 3.5 cm
Byelorussia, Mogilev-on-Dnjepr, 1800-1900
from: Byelorussia, Mogilev-on-Dnjepr

1294-18
Mezuzah
The folded piece of parchment is inserted in the glass tube, with
tin-plate loops.
Glass, parchment, tin-plate, 7.3 cm
Byelorussia, 1880-1908
from: Byelorussia, Mogilev-on-Dnjepr

1294-22
Torah mantle
A red velvet mantle embroidery with lions and the Ten
Commandments, and a Hebrew text which reads, 'Torah Crown',
followed by the initial letters of the Ten Commandments and the
year (5)630 (1870).
Velvet, silk, silver thread, 49 x 40 cm
Byelorussia, Mogilev-on-Dnjepr, 1800-1900
from: Byelorussia, Mogilev-on-Dnjepr

1294-40 b
Marriage contract
A printed marriage contract in green and gold, with Art Nouveau
decoration.
Ya.K. Lidski Publishing House
Paper, paint, 48 x 30 cm
Warsaw, 1904
from: Byelorussia, Mogilev-on-Dnjepr

1294-48
Kitchen knife
Metal kitchen knife with wooden handle (Yiddish: hak messer) for
meat and fish.
Wood, metal, 15.5 x 16 cm
Byelorussia, Mogilev-on-Dnjepr, 1880-1908
from: Byelorussia, Mogilev-on-Dnjepr

2136-1 a b
Chanukah lamp
A silver Chanukah lamp in Baroque style with seven oil pans
flanked by two lions, with flower-baskets and two birds at the
base, a crown above. The oil pans are removable.
Silver, hallmark: Tardy (1987), p.65; 33 x 25.5 x 7 cm
Austria-Hungary, Lvov (Lemberg), 1779
from: Byelorussia, Vitebsk

A.K. Serzhputovsky Collection, 1909/1923

1564-1
Tallit katan
A ritual undergarment, with horizontal black stripes and tzitzit
(fringes) at the four corners, worn by boys.
Workshop production
Wool, 104 x 44 cm, unfolded
Warsaw Province, Lovich, 1880-1900
from: Warsaw Province, Lovich

1564-6
Man's shirt
A man's shirt of fine white linen (Yiddish: kittle) with turn-down
collar; fastened with white cord. Straight, wide sleeves. Worn on
Yom Kippur and at weddings and funerals.
Cotton, 190 x 14 cm
Warsaw Province, Lovich, 1880-1900
from: Warsaw Province, Lovich

1564-7
Woman's bonnet
A bonnet (Yiddish: houb) made of black cotton lace and muslin, with gauze lining and wire frame. Decorated with green ribbon, velvet panels, lace frill. Typical headgear from the late 19th to early 20th century in the small Jewish towns of the Russian Empire.
Velvet, gauze, lace, muslin, satin ribbons, 12 x 30 cm
Warsaw Province, Lovich, 1800-1909
from: Warsaw Province, Lovich

1564-9
Woman's bonnet
A black lined bonnet covered with silk net (Yiddish: akoks). The front is decorated with multicolored textile and red feathers. The cap is decorated with beads, sequins and velvet.
Lasting, silk net, feathers, beads, sequins, hat-bands, 19 cm (diam.) x 7 cm
Warsaw Province, Lovich, 1900-1909
from: Warsaw Province, Lovich

4035-2
Woman's wig
Traditionally married women cover their hair or shave it off. In the latter case they wear a wig (Yiddish: paruk). They might also cover their head with a bonnet, a shawl or another form of headgear.
The brown hairpiece is attached to black cotton ribbons and a net. Ribbons were used for fastening the hairpiece.
Hair, artificial fibre; netting: cotton, 35 cm
Byelorussia, Minsk Province, Slutsk region, Vyzna, 1900-1920
from: Byelorussia, Minsk Province, Slutsk region, Vyzna

4035-3
Woman's wig
A wig made of natural hair. The hair is attached to black cotton ribbons, their ends used for fastening the hairpiece.
Hair, 45 cm
Byelorussia, Minsk Province, Slutsk region, Vyzna, 1900-1920
from: Byelorussia, Minsk Province, Slutsk region, Vyzna

4035-4
Woman's wig
A wig made of natural hair with two plaits. The hair is attached to black cotton ribbons, their ends used for fastening the hairpiece.
Hair, 45 cm
Byelorussia, Minsk Province, Slutsk region, Vyzna, 1900-1920
from: Byelorussia, Minsk Province, Slutsk region, Vyzna

4035-5
Woman's wig
A wig, made of natural hair with one plait.
Hair, 56 cm
Byelorussia, Minsk Province, Slutsk region, Vyzna, 1900-1920
from: Byelorussia, Minsk Province, Slutsk region, Vyzna

Collection S.A. Rapoport (An-sky), 1911-1916

5943-3/2
Synagogue lamp, fragment
Figure of a deer, made in traditional folk style of small metallic plastic art of Poland and Ukraine of the 18th, 19th centuries, characterized by common shapes and static poses.
Brass, 13.5 x 14.5 cm
Poland, 1700-1800
from: Western Ukraine, Volhynia/Podolia

5943-7
Kiddush cup
A cylindrical cup with engraved decoration of a blessing hand and a crown, two lion medallions and inscription: For Life.
Brass, 5.5 x 3.8 (base) x 5.8 cm (top)
Poland, 1700-1800
from: Western Ukraine, Volhynia/Podolia

5943-10
Chanukah lamp
Chanukah lamp for oil with snakes on the backplate and grill-work on the side pieces. Typical of a certain type of Polish/Ukrainian lamps.
Brass, 21.5 x 29.5 x 9 cm
Poland, 1700-1800
from: Western Ukraine, Volhynia/Podolia

5943-12
Synagogue lamp, fragment
Traditional folk manufacture, a sculpted lion. Typical of Polish and Western work of the 18th and 19th centuries; characterised by standard shapes and static poses.
Brass, 22.5 x 24.5 cm
Poland, 1700-1800
from: Western Ukraine, Volhynia/Podolia

5943-13
Funeral cup
A cylindrical cup with two handles and engraving with floral motif, representing vases with elaborate bouquets of flowers. Inscription reads: I am the engraver, in honour of the craver, made and completed during the weekly scriptural reading of Chukat (Num. 19-22) in the year (5)600 (11 July, 1840).
Brass, 17.5 x 18.5 x 12 cm diam.
Austria-Hungary, Galicia (?), 1846
from: Western Ukraine, Volhynia/Podolia

5943-15
Torah shield
A rectangular shield with semi-circular top; engraving of flowers in vases with leaves and a crown; inscription in the centre reads 'Holy for God', and the year (5)526 (1766).
Silver-plated brass, 12.5 x 12 cm
Western Ukraine, Volhynia/Podolia, 1766
from: Western Ukraine, Volhynia/Podolia

5943-17
Torah shield
A rectangular shield with semi-circular top, floral engraving, stylized branches and inscription: Holy for God.
Silver-plated brass, 11 x 10.2 cm
Western Ukraine, Volhynia/Podolia, 1700-1800
from: Western Ukraine, Volhynia/Podolia

5943-21
Torah pointer
A silver pointer with an inscription on the handle, reading:
This was donated by Menakhem-Mendel, son of r. Nasanil to the Mishna Society. He died on the 10th day of the month Tevet (5)635 (18 December 1874).
This was donated by the eminent Gaon Nathan Nate, head of the rabbinical court of the holy congregation of Brod, of blessed memory.
This will be for him their inheritance in Berestechko.
Passed away with a good name and went to eternity on the eve of New Moon Tamuz (5)525 (19 June 1765).
Gilded silver, 18 x 2.6 cm (diam.)
Poland, 1700-1800
from: Western Ukraine, Volhynia/Podolia

5943-22
Torah pointer
Massive pointer, with spiral-shaped handle, terminating in a lion shape bearing a ring at its back.
Silver, 25.5 x 4.5 cm
Poland, 1780-1820
from: Western Ukraine, Volhynia/Podolia

5943-25
Torah shield
A rectangular shield with floral engraving, curling branches, two small birds and an inscription in the centre: This is a gift from the Torah scholar rabbi Jakob, son of rabbi Mordechai, in the year (5)523 (1763).
Silver-plated brass, 14 x 12 cm
Western Ukraine, Volhynia/Podolia, 1763
from: Western Ukraine, Volhynia/Podolia

The synagogue in Peschanka

The Count and the Din Torah on the question of the synagogue in Mezeritch

Abraham Rechtman

When the Count of Mezeritch celebrated the wedding of his only son, lavishly distributing gifts to everyone, he also gave his consent to a long-cherished wish of the local Jewish community to build a synagogue. Since he was a devoted Catholic, the Count decided that their prayer-house would be built opposite his palace and in this way he would be able to make sure the Jews of his town were pious and prayed regularly.

However, just as he was on the point of allowing building to start, the Count fell ill and after a short while he died. Then when his son and heir arrived to take over from his father the Jews told him about his father's promise and asked him to honour it.

But the young Count had no intention to keeping his father's promise. He dismissed the Jews' request and said that his father had never told him about any such grant and, anyway he would not believe that his father, a devout Catholic, would make such a promise to Jews, the antichrist.

But that very night, as the local Jews relate, the old Count appeared to his son in his dream, and urged him to keep his promise to build a synagogue for the Jews of Mezeritch. However, considering himself a modern man and a scholar the young Count disregarded the dream and the warnings. He decided to leave town and visit other faraway places.

The Jews, however, decided to challenge the young Count with a rabbinical court. At first the young Count was extremely angry and said: 'Damn their insolence, how dare they! Must I appear before their rabbi to be cross-examined?' But his anger soon abated and he actually found the Jewish chotzpe, their daring, quite intriguing. So he appeared on the agreed date in the beth din shtibl, the rabbi's chambers, where the rabbi and two other arbitrators, seven elders and the parnassim were all seated around the table.

As the Count entered the room, with a wry smile under his neatly trimmed moustache, he turned to the men round the table and posed this crafty question: 'I ask you please, tell me how it is that you can ask me, a gentile, to build a synagogue to your God. Why can't you, with all your Jewish power, build a house for your Jewish God?'

One of the elders answered him: 'We Jews are poor. We have no land, no forests; we possess no horses and wagons and we do not own a brick factory. The Paritz, the aristocrat, is our lord and we are his subjects. So, to whom should we apply if not to you, dear lord, and especially when your noble father had promised to build us a synagogue?'

But the young Count was unmoved, his smile still in place.

Then the old grey-haired rabbi raised his bright, shining eyes and looking at the Count he said: 'Reverend Sir, the Ten Commandments are holy not only to us Jews but to you Catholics too. Surely you remember that the fifth commandment says: "Honour thy father and thy mother". So I ask you: why do break this commandment by breaking the promise made by your father, the noble Count?'

The rabbi's sharp remarks and penetrating look unsettled the young Count and he rose from his chair. He remembered now that his father had appeared in his dream commanding him to keep his promise to build the Jews a synagogue. The smile disappeared from his face; he was at a loss. Then he raised his head, looked at the rabbi respectfully, sat down again and, smiling shyly, he addressed the court in a calm voice: 'I am ready to fulfil my father's promise to you. Tell me, how much is it going to cost. Of course it would be unfair to expect me to pay for everything. The community should take a part in the project and help in the construction. I put my trust in the rabbi, he will decide what I should do; I shall follow his ruling'. Then having completed his speech, the Count rose, bowed to the rabbi and left the room.

The judgement was as follows: the Count would provide the raw materials and the necessary machinery; the Jews the work force.

The Count fulfilled his side of the bargain to the letter; he even ordered his own architect to supervise the project. The Jews worked for months until the synagogue of Mezeritch was finished.

5943-27
Torah shield
A square shield with semi-circular top, decorated with a floral motif and crown.
Silver-plated brass, 27 x 10 cm
Western Ukraine, Volhynia/Podolia, 1800-1900
from: Western Ukraine, Volhynia/Podolia

5943-28
Torah shield
A square shield with semi-circular top, floral engraving, two lions and inscription in the centre: This was donated by Elia Meir on behalf of his son, the child Arje Leib.
Metal, 11.7 x 8.8 cm
Western Ukraine, Volhynia/Podolia, 1700-1800
from: Western Ukraine, Volhynia/Podolia

5943-37
Torah shield
A rectangular shield with semi-circular top; decoration and engraving of leaves, flowers, lions, a crown and gryphons. The inscription refers to a circumcision: This is a donation of Zvi, son of Shabtai for his son Idel Elijah, may God let him grow up for Torah, marriage and goods deeds, in the year (5)568 (1808).
Silver plated brass, 13.5 cm x 12.5 cm
Western Ukraine, Volhynia/Podolia, 1808
from: Western Ukraine, Volhynia/Podolia

5943-39
Torah shield
A rectangular shield with a decoration and engraving of branches, leaves and an inscription, referring to a circumcision: This is a donation of the prominent rabbi Gedalya, on behalf of his son Dov, may God let him grow up for Torah, marriage and good deeds, amen.
Silver-plated brass, 12.7 x 9.7 cm
Western Ukraine, Volhynia/Podolia, 1800-1825
from: Western Ukraine, Volhynia/Podolia

5943-41
Torah shield
A rectangular shield, with semi-circular top. The circular central panel is flanked by two deer and stylized branches, with leaves and flowers. The lower corners bear 'Baroque' shells. The inscription reads: Sabbath, in the year (5)538 (1778).
Silver-plated brass, 15.5 x 13.6 cm
Western Ukraine, Volhynia/Podolia, 1778 (?)
from: Western Ukraine, Volhynia/Podolia

5943-42
Torah shield
Square shield, with semi-circular top and floral and geometric decoration; the inscription in the centre reads: Sabbath.
Brass, 16.2 x 13 cm
Western Ukraine, Volhynia/Podolia, 1800-1820
from: Western Ukraine, Volhynia/Podolia

5943-59
Amulet
Medallion-shaped amulet, representing Moses with the Tablets of the Law. There is an inscription on the back. Worn as a neck ornament. This type of mass-produced amulet became popular among the Jewish population of Russia in the late 19th and early 20th century, in imitation of the crosses worn by Christians.
Silver, enamel, 2 x 1.8 (diam.) cm
Russia, Ukraine, 1880-1910
from: Western Ukraine, Volhynia/Podolia

5943-67
Chanukah lamp
The lamp consists of two parts: a brass open-work plate of early origin, (probably 15th century, Italy), and a stepped black marble base of later date. It contains the usual inscription: For the commandment is a lamp, and the law is a light (Prov. 6:23).
Brass, marble, 22 x 30.5 cm
Western Europe (possibly Italy), 1400-1500 (?)
from: Western Ukraine, Volhynia/Podolia

5943-68
Chanukah lamp
Two sides and front lattice of a Chanukah lamp. They represent the classical type of Polish Chanukah lamps of the 18th century repeating architectural synagogical forms.
(Together with 6802-21)
Brass, 26.5 x 31.5 cm
Poland, 1700-1800
from: Western Ukraine, Volhynia/Podolia

5943-71
Torah pointer
Gilded hand-shaped pointer, with a long thin handle, terminating in a ball and a loop.
Silver, gilded hallmark: Tardy (1987), p.65; 16.2 x 2.5 cm (diam.)
Austria-Hungary, Galicia (?), 1830
from: Western Ukraine, Volhynia/Podolia

5943-73
Torah shield
Square shield, background covered with floral pattern, the centre bearing a Baroque cartouche, with engraved inscription, that reads: This is the donation of rabbi Jacob, for the child Pinchas Ber. Because of this, may God let him grow up for Torah, marriage and good deeds, amen.
Silver-plated metal, 14.5 x 12.5 cm
Western Ukraine, Volhynia/Podolia, 1880-1920
from: Western Ukraine, Volhynia/Podolia

5943-76
Synagogue lamp, fragment
A brass fragment of a synagogue lamp with decorations: a double-headed crowned eagle, two deer and a lion. Surrounded with interweaving leaves and bunches of grapes.
Brass, 19.5 x 52 cm
Poland, 1700-1800 (?)
from: Western Ukraine, Volhynia/Podolia

5943-77
Menorah
A menorah with seven oil pans. Rectangular backplate, with rounded top, decorated with a Star of David. The oil pans are cylindrical. The backplate and the shelf are connected by a decorative bracket of thin wire.
Tin-plate, brass, wire, 49.7 x 39.2 x 20 cm
Western Ukraine, Volhynia/Podolia, 1800-1900
from: Western Ukraine, Volhynia/Podolia

5943-79
Chanukah lamp
A brass Chanukah lamp with floral decoration and birds. Triangular open-work backplate finished with an oval loop. Deep oil pans. This type of brass casting is characteristic of Polish and Ukrainian craftspeople.
Brass, 17 x 19 x 7 cm
Poland, 1700-1800
from: Western Ukraine, Volhynia/Podolia

5943-81
Spicebox
Oval spicebox surmounted by a tiny sacrificial lamb.
Silver, hallmark: Tardy (1987), p.328; 7.1 x 3 (diam.) cm
Poland, 1845-1847
from: Western Ukraine, Volhynia/Podolia

5943-82
Spicebox
The box is shaped like a bird sitting on a bent branch. The bird motif is a characteristic feature of Polish and Ukrainian objects of this kind.
Silver, hallmark: Tardy (1987), p.328; 8.9 x 7.5 cm
Poland, 1800-1850
from: Western Ukraine, Volhynia/Podolia

5943-88
Kiddush cup
A cup with engraved decoration of a cartouche, supported by
two lions, and blessing hands; a crown and inscription in the
cartouche reading: Holy, sabbath.
Silver, hallmark: Tardy (1987), p.65; 6.6 x 4 (base) x 5.8 (top) cm
Austria-Hungary, Galicia, 1830
from: Western Ukraine, Volhynia/Podolia

5943-90
Passover cup
A cup with a decoration in relief of the Exodus, and an
inscription: Memory of the Exodus from Egypt.
Silver, 8.5 x 6.2 (diam.) cm
Poland, 1800-1900
from: Western Ukraine, Volhynia/Podolia

5943-91
Kiddush cup
Cup with a domed lid, surmounted by a rosette and a bird.
Gilded silver, hallmark: Tardy (1987), pp.60, 62; two other
marks unidentified; 23.4 x 9 (diam.) cm x 7.5 cm (base)
Austria-Hungary, 1740-1760
from: Western Ukraine, Volhynia/Podolia

5943-100
Mezuzah
Oval container with floral filigree ornamentation.
Silver, 12 x 5.5 cm
Poland, 1800-1820
from: Western Ukraine, Volhynia/Podolia

5943-105
Spicebox
This spicebox or spice tower has an architectural design with a
pointed roof and pennants, the whole construction standing on
a ball, with a stepped base. Both the form of the object and the
technique are characteristic of Polish and Ukrainian masters.
Silver, 19.5 x 5.5 x 5.5 cm
Poland, 1800-1920
from: Western Ukraine, Volhynia/Podolia

5943-106
Spicebox
This box is shaped like a sunflower on a curled stem with leaves.
It is characteristic of a certain type of Polish and Ukrainian work.
Silver, hallmark: Tardy (1987), p.365; master's mark not
identified; 16.6 x 6 (diam.) cm
Poland or Russia, 1700-1800
from: Western Ukraine, Volhynia/Podolia

5943-107
Spicebox
This spicebox has the shape of a bird sitting on a pear. Decorated
with motifs of fruit, flowers and birds. This combination is
characteristic of a certain group of objects, manufactured by
Polish and Ukrainian masters.
Silver, hallmark: Tardy (1987), p.328; 13.5 x 7 x 5 cm
Poland, 1880-1920
from: Western Ukraine, Volhynia/Podolia

5943-109
Spicebox
The pear-shaped box rests upon a curving leafy branch topped
by a small bird.
Silver, 13.9 x 8.5 x 6.5 cm
Poland, 1800-1900
from: Western Ukraine, Volhynia/Podolia

5943-111
Spicebox
A spice box in the shape of a stylized flower bud, with a floral
rosette and small bird on the lid.
Silver, 12 x 4 cm
Poland, 1840-1860
from: Western Ukraine, Volhynia/Podolia

5943-112
Spicebox
Drum-shaped box, with fretwork holes and conical lid.
Silver, hallmark: Tardy (1987), p.365; second mark unidentified;
9.5 x 4.1 (base) cm
Poland or Russia, 1800-1900
from: Western Ukraine, Volhynia/Podolia

5943-115
Spicebox
Multi-sided box, with small holes and conical lid, having a short
stem and square base.
Silver, hallmark: Tardy (1987), p.328; 8.3 x 2.5 (base) cm
Poland, 1845
from: Western Ukraine, Volhynia/Podolia

5943-116
Spicebox
Six-sided spice tower, the panels decorated with flat open-work
and figured pendants. The lid has a pointed pyramid shape
topped with a pennant. The base is circular.
Silver, hallmark: POB, not identified; 23 cm
Eastern Europe (?), 1800-1900
from: Western Ukraine, Volhynia/Podolia

5943-118
Spicebox
Spherical box, girdled with openwork belt, the conical lid topped
by a pennant. Set on a stem, with a hollow ball in the centre. The
stepped base is decorated in openwork lattice with a design
resembling that of the belt of the box.
Silver, 15.4 x 5 (diam.) cm
Poland, 1800-1900
from: Western Ukraine, Volhynia/Podolia

5943-119
Spicebox
An oval box with removable lid and base.
Silver, 4.6 x 3 (diam.) cm
Western Europe, 1700-1800
from: Western Ukraine, Volhynia/Podolia

5943-125
Amulet ring
An amulet ring with inscription in Hebrew which is
undecipherable.
Silver, 0.5 x 2 (diam.) cm
Western Ukraine, Volhynia/Podolia, 1800-1900
from: Western Ukraine, Volhynia/Podolia

6396-3
Man's coat
Outdoor garment of a tsadik from the town of Kaidonov, made
of light textile, with a fine pattern and red cord. The cut is straight,
loose, with additional gores at the skirt and an upright stitched
collar. The sleeves are fastened with buttons, the skirt with tapes.
Worn together with a belt and fur hat, typical for Ukrainian and
Polish Chassidim.
Cotton, linen, 132 x 540 x 61 cm
Western Ukraine, Kaidanov, 1800-1900
from: Western Ukraine, Kaidanov

6396-4
Belt with buckle
Yom Kippur belt with silver buckle with engraved floral
decoration. The floral ornament was characteristic for Polish
and Ukrainian goldsmiths of the 18th to early 19th century.
Brocade, silver; belt 130 x 7.5 cm; buckle 20.5 x 6.4 cm
Poland, 1700-1820
from: Western Ukraine, Volhynia/Podolia

6396-5
Bowl
Richly decorated washbowl. Ornamentation includes birds, fish,
branches and flowers. The Hebrew inscription reads: 'Joseph is a
wild ass, a wild ass by a spring, wild colts on a hillside' (Gen.
49:22).
Brass, 14.5 x 12 cm (base) x 16 cm (top)
Western Ukraine, Volhynia/Podolia, 1700-1800
from: Western Ukraine, Volhynia/Podolia

Jews of Vilna region, 19th century

6396-6
Torah binder, fragment
A binder (Yiddish: wimpeln) of green-blue silk, with an
unidentified Hebrew text embroidered in silk and metal thread.
Silk, metal thread, 64 x 8.5 cm
Western Ukraine, Volhynia/Podolia, 1800-1900
from: Western Ukraine, Volhynia/Podolia

6396-7
Skullcap
Silk skullcap with double brocade (shpanyer) trimming. This
skullcap belonged to a tsadik from the small town of Yampol.
Silk, metal thread, cotton, 15 x 19 cm (diam.)
Western Ukraine, Volhynia/Podolia, 1800-1900
from: Western Ukraine, Volhynia/Podolia

6396-8
Skullcap
Skullcap with silver thread embroidery.
Silk, metal thread, leather, 16 x 20 cm (diam.)
Western Ukraine, Volhynia/Podolia, 1880-1920
from: Western Ukraine, Volhynia/Podolia

6396-13
Woman's bodice piece
A decoration worn with a festive dress (Yiddish: brustichel). A
rectangular piece of silk is sewn over a cardboard backing, with
three vertical stripes of metallic galloon. A linen lining and similar
textile strip is attached to the lower edge. This article covered the
front of a blouse and jacket; at the upper end, tapes were fastened
round the neck, while the lower edge was tucked under a belt,
skirt, or apron.
Cardboard, linen, silk, gold-thread braid, 44.5 x 18 cm
Western Ukraine, Volhynia/Podolia, 1800-1900
from: Western Ukraine, Volhynia/Podolia

6396-14
Woman's bodice piece
A decoration worn with a festive dress (Yiddish: brustichel)
decorated with golden threads and spangles. Trimmed with strips
of brocade (shpanyer).
Cardboard, cotton, velvet, gold thread, spangles, 35 x 11 cm
Western Ukraine, Volhynia/Podolia, 1800-1900
from: Western Ukraine, Volhynia/Podolia

6396-15
Woman's bodice piece
This garment has a central vertical strip of old-brocade, decorated
with spangles and foil applique, flanked by two strips of brocade,
or 'shpanyer'.
Cardboard, cotton, velvet, metal thread, brocade, foil, spangles,
33 x 6.5 cm
Western Ukraine, Volhynia/Podolia, 1700-1850
from: Western Ukraine, Volhynia/Podolia

6396-16
Woman's bodice piece
This garment is conically shaped and has metallic embroidery
in a floral design.
Silk, gold thread, linen, 22.5 x 6 cm
Western Ukraine, Volhynia/Podolia, 1700-1825
from: Western Ukraine, Volhynia/Podolia

6396-17
Woman's bodice piece
This garment is conically shaped and has metallic embroidery,
in a floral design.
Velvet, silk, gold thread, spangles, 29 x 16.5 cm
Western Ukraine, Volhynia/Podolia, 1700-1850
from: Western Ukraine, Volhynia/Podolia

6396-18
Woman's bodice piece
A decoration worn over the bodice, rather like a kerchief, made of
fine silk, with black squares at the corners. Such a 'brustichel' was
attached near the collar with the help of a cameo brooch.
Silk, 42 x 42 cm
Western Ukraine, Volhynia/Podolia, 1800-1900
from: Western Ukraine, Volhynia/Podolia

6396-19
Woman's cap
Round black velvet cap (Yiddish: houb) with silk fringe (long at
the back and short in front) and red woollen ring at the top, sewn
down with metallic tape.
Velvet, silk and wool threads, metal threads, cotton, 55 cm x 22 cm
(diam.)
Western Ukraine, Volhynia/Podolia, 1800-1900
from: Western Ukraine, Volhynia/Podolia

6396-20
Woman's wig fillet
Married woman's wig, rectangular shaped, with bands. The
central part is flat, the sides organized in three scallops, the
stitches being covered with plaited cords. The front of the wig is
similarly decorated. The oldest type of wig, known from the 18th
century in these parts.
Satin, gauze, wadding, cord, 48 x 13 cm
Western Ukraine, Volhynia/Podolia, 1800-1900
from: Western Ukraine, Volhynia/Podolia

6396-23
Woman's wig
Female headgear resembling a bonnet; of dark cotton, with metal
wire frame used as a plait or bun container. Worn with a head-
kerchief or hat.
Cotton, metal wire, 21 x 10 cm (diam.)
Western Ukraine, Volhynia/Podolia, 1800-1920
from: Western Ukraine, Volhynia/Podolia

6396-24/1-2
Woman's shoes
A pair of festive slippers made of brown silk; metallic thread
embroidery, spangles and foil applique. Decorated with small
silk rosette and metal bead. Leather sole, black cotton lining.
Leather, silk, gold thread, foil, spangles, 23 x 7 x 5 cm
Western Ukraine, Volhynia/Podolia, 1880-1900
from: Western Ukraine, Volhynia/Podolia

6396-26
Torah mantle
Silk mantle with silken embroidery in floral pattern.
Silk, cotton, metallic threads, silk fringe, 81 x 37 cm
Western Ukraine, Volhynia/Podolia, 1800-1900
from: Western Ukraine, Volhynia/Podolia

6396-31
Woman's bodice piece
A decoration for a festive dress, with metallic thread embroidery,
spangles and foil applique; flanked by two strips of brocade
(Yiddhish: shpanyer).
Silk, brocade, silver, gold thread, 41 x 8.5 cm
Western Ukraine, Volhynia/Podolia, 1800-1920
from: Western Ukraine, Volhynia/Podolia

6396-32
Woman's bodice piece
A bodice decoration for a festive dress with a green velvet vertical
panel in the centre, decorated with metallic embroidery and
spangles. The panel is edged with two strips of 'shpanyer'.
Cardboard, velvet, silk, gold thread, spangles, cotton, 35 x 7 cm
Western Ukraine, Volhynia/Podolia, 1800-1900
from: Western Ukraine, Volhynia/Podolia

6396-33
Woman's bodice piece
A bodice decoration for a festive dress with brocade (Western
Europe, 18th-19th century) panel in the centre, edged with two
strips of 'shpanyer'. Rectangular piece of cotton sewn at the
bottom.
Cardboard, brocade, cotton, 41 x 9 cm
Western Ukraine, Volhynia/Podolia, 1700-1900
from: Western Ukraine, Volhynia/Podolia

6396-34

Woman's bodice piece

A bodice decoration for a festive dress with brocade section (Western Europe, 18th-19th century), decorated with spangles, metal threads, foil applique, edged with two strips of 'shpanyer'.
Cardboard, silk, linen, gold thread, spangles, foil, 37.5 x 11.5 cm
Western Ukraine, Volhynia/Podolia, 1900-1920
from: Western Ukraine, Volhynia/Podolia

6396-35

Woman's bodice piece

A bodice decoration for a festive dress, made of silk, the front covered with brocade.
Cardboard, silk, linen, gold thread, 31 x 7 cm
Western Ukraine, Volhynia/Podolia, 1900-1920
from: Western Ukraine, Volhynia/Podolia

6396-38

Skullcap

Skullcap (Yiddish: yarmulka) for special occasions, with six silk gores, decorated with metallic embroidery, the connecting stitches covered with metallic cord.
Silk, metal threads, foil, spangles, metallic cord, 14 x 19 cm (diam.)
Western Ukraine, Volhynia/Podolia, 1800-1900
from: Western Ukraine, Volhynia/Podolia

6396-41

Torah ark valance

Silk and brocade valance (Hebrew: caporet), with tassels of metal and wool; an undecipherable Hebrew text.
Silk, brocade, metallic thread, wool, 92 x 15 cm
Western Ukraine, Volhynia/Podolia, 1700-1800
from: Western Ukraine, Volhynia/Podolia

6396-43

Skullcap

Skullcap (Yiddish: yarmulka) for festival wear, with six brocade gores, each embroidered with a garland and a bunch of flowers; foil applique and spangles. Edged with brocade.
Brocade, metallic thread, foil, spangles, 11.5 x 19.0 (diam.) cm
Western Ukraine, Volhynia/Podolia, 1800-1900
from: Western Ukraine, Volhynia/Podolia

6396-46

Torah ark valance

Torah ark valance (Hebrew: caporet) of red silk, decorated with metallic work, representing three crowns and two double-head eagles; scallops with stylized monograms. Hebrew inscription: Crown of Torah. Crown of priests. Crown of kingship (Mishna Avot 4:17). And thou shalt put the ark cover above upon the ark (Ex. 25:21).
Silk, linen, metal thread, 62 x 32 cm
Western Ukraine, Volhynia/Podolia, 1700-1800
from: Western Ukraine, Volhynia/Podolia

6396-48

Print

Folk print or 'lubok' showing David and Goliath. The Hebrew text reads: This is the battle of Goliath the Philistine with King David. Above the picture of a group of Jews is the word: 'Israel'; above a group of soldiers is the word: 'Philistines'.
Paper, watercolour, Indian ink, 32.5 x 40.8 cm
Western Ukraine, Volhynia/Podolia, 1880-1915
from: Western Ukraine, Volhynia/Podolia

6396-49

Print

Folk print or 'lubok' showing angels guiding Lot out of Sodom, with a text in Yiddish: How the angel led Lot forth from Sodom with his wife and two daughters and how his wife looked behind her and so was turned into a pillar of salt and how the daughters made their father Lot drunk (Gen. 19).
Paper, watercolour, Indian ink, 33 x 43.5 cm
Western Ukraine, Volhynia/Podolia, 1800-1910
from: Western Ukraine, Volhynia/Podolia

6396-50

Print

Folk print or 'lubok' concerning Passover with a text in Hebrew, derived from the Hagadah: 'About four sons tells the Torah – the wise, the wicked, the simple and the one who does not know to ask'.
Paper, watercolour, Indian ink, 32 x 43.5 cm
Western Ukraine, Volhynia/Podolia, 1800-1915
from: Western Ukraine, Volhynia/Podolia

6396-51

Print

Folk print or 'lubok' showing Balaam and the ass, with a text in Yiddish: And the ass sees that this is the angel of the Lord, barring the way. And Balaam's anger is kindled and he hit the ass with a staff (cf. Num. 22:23-27).
Paper, watercolour, Indian ink, 32 x 43.5 cm
Western Ukraine, Volhynia/Podolia, 1800-1915
from: Western Ukraine, Volhynia/Podolia

6396-52

Print

Folk print or 'lubok' showing Rebecca and Eliezer, with a Yiddish text reading: This is Rebecca, giving water to the camels, and Eliezer the servant of Abraham, bowing down to thank the Lord (cf. Gen. 24:17-27).
Paper, watercolour, Indian ink, 32 x 43.5 cm
Western Ukraine, Volhynia/Podolia, 1880-1910
from: Western Ukraine, Volhynia/Podolia

6396-53

Print

Folk print or 'lubok' showing the funeral of Jacob. The Yiddish text reads: These are the sons of Jacob who bring their father to the land of Canaan to bury him; Joseph goes together with all the elders of the land of Egypt (cf. Gen. 50:1-9).
Paper, watercolour, Indian ink, 32 x 43.5 cm
Western Ukraine, Volhynia/Podolia, 1880-1910
from: Western Ukraine, Volhynia/Podolia

6396-54

Belt with buckle

White cotton belt, with red cross-stitch embroidery, edged with green strips. Circular openwork buckle, with central rosette. The inscription refers to the fact that this belt was worn on the Day of Atonement. It reads: For that day shall the priest make an atonement for you to cleanse you, that you may be clean from all your sins before the Lord (Lev. 16:30), the year (5)641 (1881). May you be recorded and sealed into a good year.
Cotton, woollen thread, silver, 104 x 4.5 cm
Western Ukraine, Volhynia/Podolia, 1881
from: Western Ukraine, Volhynia/Podolia

6396-55

Omer calendar

An omer calendar in a wooden case, the carved decoration having a floral pattern and two lions in the upper part.
Wood, paper, glass, 14.8 x 7 x 4.8 cm
Western Ukraine, Volhynia/Podolia, 1880-1910
from: Western Ukraine, Volhynia/Podolia

6396-58/1-2

Woman's dress

A Jewish woman's dress consisting of two required items: skirt and blouse (Yiddish: jupkie and kofta), made of pink silk. A straight, loose blouse, with hidden buttons, flat round collar, with jabot at the breast; jabot and other edges decorated with metallic tape. Wide, pleated skirt. The dress was worn together with an apron.
Silk, cotton ribbon, metallic thread, 63 x 49 x 56 (blouse) cm
Western Ukraine, Volhynia/Podolia, 1800-1900
from: Western Ukraine, Volhynia/Podolia

The synagogue of Lovich

The synagogue of Olik: built simultaneously with a church

Abraham Rechtman

The Count of the shtetl Olik, was a wicked and vicious man. He mistreated his own peasants and never allowed the Jews to get away with anything. Time and again the Jews petitioned him, asking permission to build a synagogue, but, just as he denied his peasants the right to build a church, the Count repeatedly refused their request.

One day it happened that the Count became seriously ill. All the best physicians from the big city were summoned to his bedside, but to no avail; on the contrary, his situation worsened as the days passed and his life began to ebb away. Then the Count sent for the priest and asked him to pray to God for a cure. He promised the priest that if God would listen to his prayer and if he would recover he would build the church. However, the Count's health did not improve. He felt his strength continue to ebb and his life near its end. Finally, the Count ordered emissaries to go and fetch the rabbi, and to ask him to pray for the his recovery. Again he made a promise: if the rabbi's prayer were answered he would build a synagogue for the Jews. And it happened that immediately after he gave his word to the rabbi, the Count began to feel better and after a couple of days he was totally cured. Leaving his sickbed, the Count did not forget his promises, neither to the Christians, nor to the Jews, and he was determined to fulfil both their requests. Yet he could not decide which of the two promises he should keep first: if he began with the church, the Jews would complain; if he started with the synagogue, the Christians would feel wronged. Eventually he hit upon an ingenious solution; the Count ordered the two buildings to be built simultaneously.

And so, the masons followed the Count's orders. They dug holes in the ground for both buildings simultaneously and began laying the foundations. Then they laid one brick on a wall of the church and the next on the synagogue's. After a short while both buildings were completed: they looked identical.

It was said that when the church and the synagogue were finally finished, the Count came to have a look. Observing and inspecting the buildings, he could not stop looking at them, the architecture was so sublime. The Count left the place very troubled. The next day he called for the architect and had him put to death. The Count could not bear the thought that this architect might be invited by another Count anywhere else to build anything as wonderful.

A young Jewish woman wearing 'jupkie' and 'kofta'

6396-59
Woman's blouse
A blouse (Yiddish: kofta) made of dark-green silk, with black strips, decorated with posies and flowers. No fastenings, circular opening. The sides and back flare out and have triangular scalloped edging. Sleeves also flare down to the cuff. Decorated with black cotton lace; fastened with four buttons.
Silk, cotton, 59 x 78 x 54 cm
Western Ukraine, Volhynia/Podolia, 1880-1900
from: Western Ukraine, Volhynia/Podolia

6396-61
Woman's wig fillet
This wig is of textile, imitating wavy hair; worn by married women instead of a wig of natural hair, together with a head-kerchief or bonnet and ornaments. This is an old example of a 'wig', common in Poland and southwest Russia in the 18th century.
Silk, silk thread, gauze, 58 x 12 cm
Western Ukraine, Volhynia/Podolia, 1880-1910
from: Western Ukraine, Volhynia/Podolia

6396-62
Woman's wig fillet
A piece of rectangular textile.
Satin, gauze, 40 x 11 cm
Western Ukraine, Volhynia/Podolia, 1880-1900
from: Western Ukraine, Volhynia/Podolia

6396-63
Woman's wig fillet
A rectangular piece of textile worn on the head, the ends netted together. The stitching on the scallops covered with plaited lace.
Silk, wadding, gauze, 57 x 14 cm
Western Ukraine, Volhynia/Podolia, 1800-1900
from: Western Ukraine, Volhynia/Podolia

6396-66
Woman's kerchief
A veil made of fine silken net, with rhomboid central section, ending in long strips, often fastened at the back. Chain-stitch embroidery representing floral motifs.
Silk, 118 x 21 cm
Western Ukraine, Volhynia/Podolia, 1880-1900
from: Western Ukraine, Volhynia/Podolia

6396-67
Woman's apron
A festive apron of silk voile, with machine embroidery in floral pattern and with a silken ribbon belt.
Silk, 86 x 87 cm
Western Ukraine, Volhynia/Podolia, 1800-1900
from: Western Ukraine, Volhynia/Podolia

6396-68
Woman's apron
A festive apron of light silk, embroidered with metallic thread in floral pattern. Edged with metallic tape and a fringe. The belt decorated with metallic tape.
Silk, silver, gold thread, 102 x 55 cm
Western Ukraine, Volhynia/Podolia, 1800-1900
from: Western Ukraine, Volhynia/Podolia

6396-69
Woman's bodice piece
Part of a bodice decoration for a festive dress, with pink velvet strips and metallic embroidery, spangles, foil applique, suggesting floral motifs.
Spangles, foil, metal thread, velvet, 22 x 6.5 cm
Western Ukraine, Volhynia/Podolia, 1800-1900
from: Western Ukraine, Volhynia/Podolia

6396-70
Woman's bodice piece
A bodice decoration for a festive dress with a vertical panel of older textile on the front side and a strip of brocade (Yiddish: shpanyer) along the upper edge.
Cardboard, printed cotton, silk, metal thread, 41 x 8.5 cm
Western Ukraine, Volhynia/Podolia, 1800-1900
from: Western Ukraine, Volhynia/Podolia

**A portrait of Leya Aronoda, made during the first Russian
ethnographic expedition in 1867 by P. Mivromtsev**

A Jewish woman, from Berdichev, 19th century

6396-71
Woman's bodice piece
A bodice decoration for a festive dress, the front covered with green velvet, metallic embroidery in the centre suggesting a lattice panel, each section having a floral design in applique work. The panel is edged with two strips of brocade (Yiddish: shpanyer).
Cardboard, velvet, metallic threads, spangles, foil, linen, 57 x 14 cm
Western Ukraine, Volhynia/Podolia, 1800-1900
from: Western Ukraine, Volhynia/Podolia

6396-72
Woman's bodice piece
A bodice decoration for a festive dress edged with dark-blue cotton; a decorative textile panel (Western Europe, 18th century) in the centre flanked by two strips of 'shpanyer'. Dark-blue cotton panel at the bottom.
Cardboard, silk, metallic threads, linen, cotton, 44 x 12 cm
Western Ukraine, Volhynia/Podolia, 1700-1900
from: Western Ukraine, Volhynia/Podolia

6396-73
Woman's kerchief
A triangular kerchief, of green velvet, the silver embroidery having floral motifs: Tree-of-Life on the lower edge and a chain of leaves and flowers around the perimeter. Edged with metallic tape, and a fringe.
Velvet, silk, metallic threads and ribbon with fringe, spangles, 66 x 30 cm
Western Ukraine, Volhynia/Podolia, 1700-1800
from: Western Ukraine, Volhynia/Podolia

6396-77
Torah ark valance
Rectangular dark-green velvet band (Hebrew: caporet), decorated with metallic work, spangles, foil applique, having floral and geometrical motifs. The upper edge and sides finished with silk tape and galloon, the lower edge with a strip of 'shpanyer' and adorned with five metallic-embroidered velvet scallops and tassels. Metal border at the upper edge.
Silk, velvet, metal threads, spangles, foil, cotton, metal, 77 x 15 cm
Western Ukraine, Volhynia/Podolia, 1800-1900
from: Western Ukraine, Volhynia/Podolia

6396-78
Torah ark curtain
The central part of this curtain (Hebrew: parochet) is of old brocade (Western Europe, 18th century), surrounded by an ochre-coloured velvet arch; metallic embroidery of deer on stylized branches and Hebrew text: In memory of the soul of our brothers: the learned rabbi Zvi Hirsch and our learned teacher Moshe Kaziner and the soul of his modest wife Miza, daughter of the learned rabbi Arje Leib Halevi - may their memory be a blessing. For their son the scholarly rabbi Yehuda Leib and his wife Lea, daughter of the learned rabbi Naftali Hirtz, may his memory be a blessing, for the souls of the above-mentioned and in memory of their son, the apple of their eyes, Yanuka Joel, may his memory be a blessing. May their souls be written into the book of eternal life. In the year (chronogram Isaiah 44:3 =) (5)511 (1751).
Velvet, brocade, metal threads, linen, 187 x 96 cm
Western Ukraine, Volhynia/Podolia, 1751
from: Western Ukraine, Volhynia/Podolia

6396-79
Torah ark curtain
A curtain with a central panel of pink brocade (Western Europe, possibly Poland, 18th century), surrounded by blue brocade arch, with oriental pattern, and cherry silk upper part. Edged with coloured tape, with fringes. The linen lining bears ink inscription (undeciphered). The design lacks the traditional symbolic and architectural elements common to such items. The decoration lies in the combination of richly embellished textiles.
Brocade, silk, galloon with fringe, linen, ink, 191 x 104 cm
Western Ukraine, Volhynia/Podolia, 1700-1800 (?)
from: Western Ukraine, Volhynia/Podolia

6396-80
Torah ark curtain
A curtain with a central dark-blue velvet panel, with silver-thread embroidery, representing a large rosette with six stylized buds and two small rosettes. The arch is made of ornamented silk (Western Europe, 18th century) of a brownish-red. The top of the central panel is decorated with a valance, with four scallops, having metallic embroidery and the text: Crown of Torah. This is a gift from the young Samuel, son of David, of blessed memory.
Velvet, silk, metal threads, linen, 217 x 114 cm
Western Ukraine, Volhynia/Podolia, 1700-1900
from: Western Ukraine, Volhynia/Podolia

6396-82
Torah ark curtain
A curtain with a central red velvet panel, having a vertical broad strip of old metallic lace (Western Europe, 18th century) and metallic embroidery at the top showing the Star of David and two bunches of flowers. The arch is made of ornamented blue cotton textile (Western Europe, 18th century).
Velvet, silk, metallic thread, linen, 172 x 110 cm
Western Ukraine, Volhynia/Podolia, 1700-1800
from: Western Ukraine, Volhynia/Podolia

6396-83
Torah ark valance
Rectangular green velvet valance, with side pieces of red silk and seven light-green silk scallops at the bottom. Decorated with metallic work. The pattern on the central panel has a crown and the Hebrew text: 'Crown of Torah. And thou shalt put the ark cover above upon the ark' (chronogram Ex. 25:21 =) (5)500 (1740). 'This is a donation of rabbi Nachson and his wife Chana for their daughter Esther. May God let her grow up for Torah and good deeds, amen'.
On the scallops: alternating double-headed eagles and lions. Edged with silk tape.
Velvet, silk, linen, metallic thread, 103 x 30 cm
Western Ukraine, Volhynia/Podolia, 1740
from: Western Ukraine, Volhynia/Podolia

6396-84
Torah mantle
A silk mantle with embroidery and Hebrew text relating to the Day of Atonement: 'For on that day shall be made an atonement for you, to cleanse you, that you may be clean from all your sins before the Lord (Lev. 16:30). Ezekiel son of Solomon-Zalman Cats. The year (5)505 (1745)'.
Silk, metallic thread, linen, 62 x 26 cm
Western Ukraine, Volhynia/Podolia, 1745
from: Western Ukraine, Volhynia/Podolia

6396-85
Torah ark valance
The front, of red silk, is decorated in metallic embroidery with two garlands and two crowns in the centre; there are five sections, each containing a garland and a crown, with an inscription (non-Jewish), imitating a monogram (unidentified). Edged with silk tape.
Silk, gold thread, coloured cord, lace, linen, 98 x 35 cm
Western Ukraine, Volhynia/Podolia, 1800-1900
from: Western Ukraine, Volhynia/Podolia

6396-91/1,2,3
Amulet
Three triangular pieces of paper with written text in Yiddish, addressing the souls of the dead and asking for help when ill (Yiddish: kvitlach). The text reads: To pray from the blessed Name, on behalf of Sarah, the daughter of Nemed, her daughter Rozil, the daughter of Sarah, her husband Josef, the son of Chaim; Sarah, her daughter, Mesy, the daughter of Rozil, her daughter Chemdah, the daughter of Sarah, her son Aharon Shlomeh, her son Abraham, her son Israel. May God give us consolation and recovery and long years of life and cure and health of the soul and healthy years and ... blessing and success.
Paper, ink, (1) 20.5 x 8 cm; (2) 19 x 5 cm; (3) 18 x 4 cm
Western Ukraine, Volhynia/Podolia, 1900-1910
from: Western Ukraine, Volhynia/Podolia

6396-99
Prayerbook
Prayerbook (siddur) with communal prayers from Dubno, with miniatures. The incomplete title page reads: This is the collection of the Claus ... from Dubno ... In the year (5)601 (1841).
Parchment, 29.5 x 20 cm
Western Ukraine, Volhynia/Podolia, 1841
from: Western Ukraine, Volhynia/Podolia

6396-100
Torah scroll, fragments
Torah scroll fragments sewn together to form a bag. When collecting items for the Jewish Museum in St Petersburg, An-sky apparently intended to display material connected with Jews' status in tsarist Russia, including pogroms. This probably explains some of the curious items in the collection, which mostly contains objects illustrating traditional culture. A purse made of a piece of a Torah scroll stands out particularly amidst the other objects which have deep roots of traditional Jewish culture.
Parchment, cotton, 28 x 29 cm
Western Ukraine, Volhynia/Podolia, 1800-1900
from: Western Ukraine, Volhynia/Podolia

6396-101
Scroll
A kabbalistic scroll with an inscription: The Tree of Sanctity. And this is Tree of Life from Ary, the righteous and the saint of blessed memory, which passed it to his disciple rabbi Chaim Vital, of blessed memory. The rabbi great and eminent in his name and his deeds rabbi Zeev Katsis, the righteous of blessed memory.
Paper, Indian ink, 435 x 54 cm
Western Ukraine, Volhynia/Podolia, 1800-1910
from: Western Ukraine, Volhynia/Podolia

6396-103
Mizrach
A paper cut-out mizrach with folk and floral decoration, lions and blessing hands and the Hebrew text: East. The seven lamps shall give you light over against candlestick (Num. 8:2). Know before whom you are standing (Berachot 28b). Before the supreme King of Kings, the Holy One, blessed be he (Mishna Avot 3:1).
Paper, watercolour, Indian ink, 41.3 x 47.3 cm
Western Ukraine, Volhynia/Podolia, 1880-1910
from: Western Ukraine, Volhynia/Podolia

6396-116
Woman's head-kerchief
Triangular kerchief (Yiddish: shleien) of dark-blue velvet, edged with a wide piece of gathered voile, decorated with white chain-stitch embroidery.
Velvet, silk thread, silk cord, 94 x 44 cm
Western Ukraine, Volhynia/Podolia, 1800-1900
from: Western Ukraine, Volhynia/Podolia

6396-119
Goblet
A blue porcelain cup, with a white square with text and decoration painted in gold. Floral bands at the top, and white cartouche in the centre, bearing an inscription: Isaak Meir, son of ... [undecipherable]
Porcelain, 15 x 11 cm
Ukraine, Volhynia, Baranovka, 1887
from: Western Ukraine, Volhynia/Podolia

6396-120/ 1-2
Woman's dress
Jewish woman's garment with skirt and blouse (Yiddish: jupkie and kofta) of brown silk, with oriental pattern; blouse has no fastenings, straight back, circular opening for the head, concealed hook fastenings. Skirt is cut on the straight, wide and pleated; worn with an apron.
Silk; skirt: 104 x 120 cm; blouse: 42 x 36 cm
Western Ukraine, Volhynia/Podolia, 1880-1900
from: Western Ukraine, Volhynia/Podolia

The synagogue of the great Rabbi Liber in Berdichev

Abraham Rechtman

The legend of the old synagogue, known as Rabbi Liber's synagogue, told by the old people of Berdichev is a lovely and beautiful story. Rabbi Liber lived in this shtetl before the days of the Baal Shem-Tov, the Be"sht (the founder of Chassidism). His father was Rabbi Abraham Ashkenazi, the Magid, or preacher, from Cracow; his mother was the grand-daughter of Rabbi Yehiel Michal, the martyr of Nemirov of 1648˙. In 1670, when the Jews were driven out of Cracow by the Poles, Rabbi Abraham Ashkenazi settled in Berdichev, then still a small shtetl, where he became the Magid. After his death in 1671, his son was appointed as the new Magid. Rabbi Liber was older than the Be"sht, but was fortunate enough to live a long and happy life and he eventually survived him. The Be"sht considered him a great tsadik, a revered pious man, and treated him with great respect. It is said that Elijah is revealed to great pious men, but with Rabbi Liber it was the other way round, he was revealed to Elijah. The Be"sht used to travel regularly to Berdichev in order to meet Rabbi Liber and especially in order to bath in his mikve, the ritual bath. His mikve still existed when our expedition visited Berdichev in 1913. Since people believed that the water in the mikve had special powers to heal eye diseases, many sick people came from far and wide to bath there.

According to tradition, Rabbi Liber was a very tall man, taller than most of the people of Berdichev; he had thick eye-brows which almost covered his eyes, and when he wanted to look at somebody he used to curl his eyebrows with his fingers and then let them drop. His beard was long and thick and reached down to his waist. He never combed his beard lest he should lose even one hair of it. The story goes that once when the Be"sht came for a visit, he asked Rabbi Liber for permission to comb his beard with his own fingers. The Be"sht swore that if he caused even one hair to fall, he would forfeit his share in the world to come. But Rabbi Liber still refused.

An old synagogue in the centre of Berdichev is named after Rabbi Liber as a result of the following story. All his life, on weekdays Rabbi Liber used to pray mincha, the noon prayer, in an open field. Once, while the rabbi was standing in the field under a tree deep in prayer, the Count passed by and was amazed to find a Jew swaying back and forth and not noticing his presence. He began to crack his whip and shouted, 'Jew, Jew'. But Rabbi Liber, being deeply occupied in prayer, heard neither the whip nor the Count's shouting. He went on praying as if nothing had happened. The Count became angry and said: 'What a chotzpe!'. He sent two of his servants to fetch the Jew and bring him to his carriage. The servants called him, spoke to him but the rabbi did not hear them. The Count was enraged and ordered them to fetch him by force. The servants obeyed, grabbed hold of the rabbi and put him in front of the Count. He began to curse the rabbi, but when the rabbi did not respond the Count grabbed the whip and hit him. The rabbi, however, went on praying, never crying out even once. The Count was amazed at the Jew's heroism; how could a person suffer such punishment and not utter a sound, let alone shout and cry. He stopped beating him, and his anger dissipated. But his curiosity began to grow, so he ordered his servant to carry the rabbi back to where he had been standing, under the tree, while he himself climbed into his carriage and patiently waited to see what would happen.

As soon as Rabbi Liber finished his prayers, he immediately walked over to the Count, bowed before him and said: 'My brother, what were you trying to ask me just then? Now I am ready to answer your questions.' The Count looked at the rabbi and asked him: 'Tell me, why did you not come when I called you?'
'How could I come to you, dear master, when I was standing before the master of masters confessing my sins. Could I just stop my prayer?'
'Why do you call me brother after I caused you so much pain?'
'I call you brother because all people are God's children. God is our father, and naturally his children are brothers to each other.'
'Are you not angry with me for having beaten you?'
'No, you did not beat me. Since I have sinned, the Almighty has punished me. You served as his messenger and thus I am not angry with you, indeed, I pity you.'
'Pity?' the Count was surprised, 'why pity me?'
'Because God has chosen you to be his messenger and to beat a human being and cause him pain.'

The Count was struck by this answer and stood there in silence. He understood that this was a man of God and he started to become afraid. He asked Rabbi Liber to forgive him for the pain he had caused and asked how he could make amends. Then Rabbi Liber said: 'If you regret what you have done and really desire to repent, promise me this: never raise your hand to hit another person. Never, ever.'
'Well, and should I not beat my serfs?; they are still my property'.
'No, you shall not raise a hand against them either. They are God's children too, and like me and you they

The synagogue in Berdichev

are the servants of God and not the servants of another servant.'

The Count bowed his head humbly and said: 'Rabbi, I promise you from now on I shall never lose my temper again; I promise never to raise a hand to anyone. And, since I caused you so much pain while you were praying to your Jewish God, on the very same spot, under that tree, I shall build you a synagogue, where you will be able to pray freely and untroubled.

The Count kept his promise, and on the spot where the rabbi had prayed his mincha prayer a synagogue was built, the one known today as 'The synagogue of the great Rabbi Liber' commemorating the miracle which happened to the rabbi.

In the old days, the synagogue was located outside the town's limits. Berdichev, however, has since expanded and in 1913, when we visited the town, the synagogue was in the heart of town.

---

* Nemirov was the town were one of the worst slaughters during the Chmielnicki pogroms took place.

6396-121
Mezuzah
A wooden rectangular-shaped case, with carved floral decoration and four columns.
Wood, 27 x 4.5 cm
Austria-Hungary (possibly the Carpathians), 1900-1910
from: Western Ukraine, Volhynia/Podolia

6396-123
Amulet
Three small leather bags, one empty tin-plate case, 22 silver coins (from one to eleven kopeks) and two brass coins, strung together on a long cord. All coins are well-worn and date from the mid 19th century.
Leather, parchment, silver, brass, cotton, 5.5 x 5.5 cm
Western Ukraine, Volhynia/Podolia, 1800-1900
from: Western Ukraine, Volhynia/Podolia

6396-129
Amulet
Popular print or 'lubok' print showing Isaac blessing Esau. The text on this amulet names angels and demons; the utterance of their names was thought to have magic power. Text: Picture of Isaac, our father, may he rest in peace, sitting on the throne and blessing his son Jacob. And Esau is coming from the field (Gen. 27, 30).
Paper, watercolour, Indian ink, 27 x 17 cm
Western Ukraine, Volhynia/Podolia, 1880-1910
from: Western Ukraine, Volhynia/Podolia

6396-130
Amulet
A popular print or 'lubok' showing Bathsheba kneeling in front of David. The text lists angels and demons, whose names were thought to have magic power. Text: Picture of King David, sitting on the throne and Bathsheba, prostrated before him and begging that Solomon his son may reign after him (cf. Kings I 1:16-17).
Paper, watercolour, Indian ink, 26 x 16.8 cm
Western Ukraine, Volhynia/Podolia, 1800-1910
from: Western Ukraine, Volhynia/Podolia

6396-133
Amulet
Medallion-shaped amulet, one side represents Moses with Tablets, the other side bears an inscription: Hear Israel; the Lord our God, the Lord is one (Deut. 6:4). These mass-produced amulets were fashionable among the Jewish population of Russia in the late 19th and early 20th century. They were worn around the neck, like the crosses worn by Christians.
Gilded silver, 2.2 x 1.8 cm
Russia, Ukraine, 1880-1910
from: Western Ukraine, Volhynia/Podolia

6396-136
Amulet
Parchment band with written text on both sides: 'to preserve unharmed and alive in the war, from the tsadik rabbi Samuel from Berezine'. Worn in battle as protection.
Parchment, Indian ink, 5.7 x 3.3 cm
Western Ukraine, Volhynia/Podolia, 1850-1910
from: Western Ukraine, Volhynia/Podolia

6396-144
Belt
Belt made of light cotton textile, with checked pattern, each section decorated with satin-stitch embroidered leaves. Worn tied over a kaftan, with the ends tucked in. Belt and kaftan are characteristic garments for a Chassidic tsadik. This one comes from the town of Kaidanov.
Cotton, silk thread, 263 x 16 cm
Western Ukraine, Volhynia/Podolia, 1800-1900
from: Western Ukraine, Volhynia/Podolia

6396-166
Woman's wig
A wig, made of natural hair, in two plaits.
Hair, 40 cm
Western Ukraine, Volhynia/Podolia, 1880-1900
from: Western Ukraine, Volhynia/Podolia

6396-167
Prayerbook
An illustrated prayer book, with communal prayers for sabbath, for tsar Alexander III (1881-1894), sounding the shofar and other prayers. The first page has the following text: This siddur was given as a gift by the synagogue in Kremenets to the Hebrew Museum founded by the Ethnographic Society named after the Baron Naftaly Hirz Ginzburg. Tuesday, the 20th of Tamuz (5)674, 1st of July 1914, Kremenets, Volhynia. Copied by Shlomo Eliezer, the son of the late Mordechai, of blessed memory.
In 1914 An-sky presented this prayerbook to the Jewish Historical Ethnographical Society in St Petersburg.
Parchment, paper, textile, leather, watercolour, Indian ink, 27 x 21.5 cm
Western Ukraine, Volhynia/Podolia, 1800-1900
from: Western Ukraine, Volhynia/Podolia, Kremenets

6396-169
Amulet
A popular print or 'lubok' illustrating Jacob's dream. The text lists the names of angels and demons. The incantation of their names was thought to have magic power. Text in Yiddish: Picture of Jacob, our father, may he rest in peace, sleeping in a certain place. And he dreamed, and behold a ladder set up on the earth, and the angels ascending and descending on it (cf. Gen. 28:12).
Paper, watercolour, Indian ink, 21.5 x 17.6 cm
Western Ukraine, Volhynia/Podolia, 1880-1910
from: Western Ukraine, Volhynia/Podolia

6802-2
Woman's blouse
Blouse made of green silk, with floral pattern (Yiddish: kofta). Loose yoke with tucks, front hooks for fastening. Decorated with tape and flowers made from similar tape. Both textile and design are characteristic of women's costume in Russia during the 19th century.
Silk, cotton, 52 x 44 x 40 cm
Western Ukraine, Volhynia/Podolia, 1800-1900
from: Western Ukraine, Volhynia/Podolia

6802-4
Man's shirt
A white shirt with cutaway sides; straight sleeves with gusset; circular, upright collar; long front with a slit and buttons. Traditional Ukrainian style.
Cotton, 118 x 62 cm
Western Ukraine, Volhynia/Podolia, 1900-1910
from: Western Ukraine, Volhynia/Podolia
It is written in the Torah, that a married woman must shave her head. This ritual is performed on the second day afther the wedding. Then a wig made of natural hair, or silk, would be worn. Silk and satin wigs could not capture the lively and springy nature of real hair. Nevertheless, woman proved inventive, tasteful and skilful and produced elegant headgear.

6802-5
Woman's wig fillet
A wig made of brown silk; rectangular silk strip, with ribbons at the ends. A flat central piece, the ends folded and scallop-shaped.
Satin, 43 x 14 cm
Western Ukraine, Volhynia/Podolia, 1800-1900
from: Western Ukraine, Volhynia/Podolia

6802-6
Woman's wig fillet
A wig made of chestnut hair with two plaits forming symmetrical buns.
Hair, 67 x 14 cm
Western Ukraine, Volhynia/Podolia, 1800-1900
from: Western Ukraine, Volhynia/Podolia

6802-15
Candlestick
A brass candlestick for two candles for sabbath with profiled, turned stem and circular base, crowned with a double-headed eagle. The pictorial motifs and manufacturing technique were characteristic of a particular group of brass objects made by Polish and Ukrainian masters of the 18th century.
Brass, 28 x 25.5 cm
Poland, 1700-1800
from: Western Ukraine, Volhynia/Podolia

6802-21
Chanukah lamp
The backplate of a chanukah lamp in the shape of a synagogue facade (together with 5943-68).
Brass, 30.5 x 21 cm
Poland, 1700-1800
from: Western Ukraine, Volhynia/Podolia

6802-31
Torah scroll
A Torah scroll presented to Grand Prince Nicolas, future Emperor Nicolas II, during his visit to Vilna on 11 November 1883, by a local Jewish Society, together with a cloth (6802-85).
Parchment, wood, ink, 190 x 13.5 cm
Vilna, 1800-1900
from: Vilna

6802-36
Torah crown
A silver Torah crown with two-headed eagle and decorations. There are two parts: larger lower crown and small top one. The base is formed by a brass hoop, with silver bracket plates. It shows the biblical patriarchs and kings: Moses, Abraham, Aaron, Jacob, David and Solomon. The plates alternate with six brass ribs covered with silver plaques which are decorated with floral ornaments, two-headed eagles and other birds. The upper ends of the ribs are soldered to a flat silver hoop, bearing an inscription and a small crown, also with ribs bearing silver plates. The brass plate is covered with an eight-pointed silver rosette, having a two-headed eagle in the centre. The inscription reads: This was donated by a group of servants of our community to the great synagogue here in Liotsky (?).
Silver, brass, 26.8 x 11.5 cm (diam.)
Poland, 1800-1900
from: Western Ukraine, Volhynia/Podolia

6802-37/6802-38
Torah finials
A pair of silver cylindrical rimonim with engraving in a floral pattern and a crown, bird and bell at the top. The inscription reads: This stave belongs to the burial society of the Klaus synagogue. Year (5)574 (1814). [The date on one rimonim is: Year (5)570 (1810)]
Gilded silver, 23.5 x 12.5 (base) cm
Poland, 1800-1814
from: Western Ukraine, Volhynia/Podolia

6802-39
Chanukah lamp
Gilded silver backplate decorated with a cartouche in the centre and a crown in relief; two gryphons at the top. The cartouche is decorated with a plated silver crown, central two-headed eagle and two birds and is flanked by two large curling branches and two 'Paradise' trees with the birds. An oil-jug is suspended above the cartouche; three stylized trees are placed between the back and the oil-containers, bearing a unicorn, an eagle and a deer.
Gilded silver, 26.8 x 29.5 x 7.5 cm
Poland, 1780-1820
from: Western Ukraine, Volhynia/Podolia

6802-42
Spicebox
A small spicebox in the shape of a rose with stem and leaves, a bird on top.
Silver, hallmark: Tardy (1987), p.328; 11.9 x 5.7 x 5 cm
Poland, 1800-1850
from: Western Ukraine, Volhynia/Podolia

6802-43 a,b
Spicebox
A spicebox in the shape of a poppy on a long stem, with a flat triangular base and the text: R. Israel Loitin. Made in performance of the commandment of generosity. Year (5)614 (1854).
Silver, 15.5 x 7 x 4.5 cm
Poland, 1840-1860
from: Western Ukraine, Volhynia/Podolia

6802-48 a, b
Spicebox
A circular spicebox like a bell, partly engraved and with a small bird on top.
Silver, 6 x 6 (diam.) cm
Poland, 1800-1900
from: Western Ukraine, Volhynia/Podolia

6802-50
Spicebox
A conical spicebox on a base, with a small bird on top.
Silver, 7.8 x 3.2 (diam.) cm
Poland, 1800-1900
from: Western Ukraine, Volhynia/Podolia

6802-54
Kiddush cup
A kiddush cup on three legs, with engraved geometric decoration.
Silver, hallmark: Tardy (1987), p.328; 11.3 x 6 (diam.) cm
Poland, 1800-1850
from: Western Ukraine, Volhynia/Podolia

6802-56
Kiddush cup
A cylindrical cup, with engraved floral ornaments and inscription: 'Yehuda, son of rabbi Moses Kats'. This kiddush cup is an example of the work of local masters.
Silver, hallmark: unidentified; 9.8 x 5.6 (base) x 7.4 (top) cm
Western Ukraine, Volhynia/Podolia, 1780-1820
from: Western Ukraine, Volhynia/Podolia

6802-59
Kiddush cup
A cylindrical cup with engraved decoration of three medallions with a lion and trees. This kiddush cup is an example of local craftsmanship.
Silver, 9 x 8.9 (diam.) x 5.5 cm
Western Ukraine, Volhynia/Podolia, 1780-1820
from: Western Ukraine, Volhynia/Podolia

6802-61
Kiddush cup
A cup on a circular hollow stem, with a square flat base; engraved decoration of floral rosette.
Silver, hallmark: not identified; 9.1 x 4.5 (base) x 4.7 cm (top)
Poland, 1800-1900
from: Western Ukraine, Volhynia/Podolia

6802-63
Mezuzah
Long narrow container, with engraved letter 'shin' and an opening at the upper end.
Silver, 12.4 x 1.3 cm
Poland, 1800-1900
from: Western Ukraine, Volhynia/Podolia

6802-66
Amulet ring
An amulet ring with an untranslatable Hebrew inscription inside.
Silver, 0.6 x 2 cm
Western Ukraine, Volhynia/Podolia, 1800-1900
from: Western Ukraine, Volhynia/Podolia

6802-67 /1,2
Woman's earrings
The earrings are in the shape of a small arc, with a drop-shaped pendant, framed in an oval. Worn together with headdress and wig, the extended shape was the most popular among Jewish women.
Russian mass production
Silver, 4 x 2 cm
Russia, 1800-1900
from: Western Ukraine, Volhynia/Podolia

A Jewish woman, 19th century. She is wearing beautiful earrings

6802-69
Amulet
A small medallion with Star of David and an inscription on one side, and a lion and unicorn supporting a shield with a crown, on the other. The inscription below reads: Holy Israel our King.
Silver, 2.5 cm (diam.)
Russia, Ukraine, 1880-1910
from: Western Ukraine, Volhynia/Podolia

6802-70
Amulet
Medallion-shaped amulet, representing Moses, with the Tablets of the Law and on the other side an inscription: Hear, O Israel, the Lord our God, the Lord is one.
Gilded silver, 2 x 1.9 cm
Russia, Ukraine, 1880-1920
from: Western Ukraine, Volhynia/Podolia

6802-74 /1,2
Woman's earrings
Leaf-shaped earrings worn together with headgear and wig; Russian mass production of the 19th to early 20th century.
Silver, 3.5 x 1.8 cm
Russia, 1800-1900
from: Western Ukraine, Volhynia/Podolia

6802-82
Scroll of Esther
Esther scroll, in a cylindrical engraved silver case. The design of the case consists of three bands, the central one decorated with floral ornament. The ends show rows of stylized two-headed eagles and openwork garlands.
Parchment, silver, 19 x 3.5 cm (case)
Poland, 1800-1850
from: Western Ukraine, Volhynia/Podolia

6802-83
Circumcision knife in case
The knife used in circumcision by the 'mohel'. The handle is of semi-precious stone, decorated with silver and small garnets and two pieces of gold alloy . The Hebrew text reads: 'Blessed art thou, Lord our God, King of the Universe who hast sanctified us with thy commandments, and commanded us concerning circumcision. Blessed art thou, Lord our God, King of the Universe, who hast sanctified us with thy commandments, and commanded us to introduce my son into the covenant of Abraham our father'.
The accompanying box is lined with dark-blue velvet.
Silver, garnets, chalcedony, gold alloy, steel, 13.5 x 2.5 cm
Poland (?), 1840-1860
from: Western Ukraine, Volhynia/Podolia

6802-85
Decorative cloth
A cotton cloth with cross-stitch embroidery in a folk design and a text in Russian: 11 November 1883 from Vilna Jewish Society. This cloth was presented together with a Torah scroll (6802-31) to the Crown Prince Nicolas, afterwards Emperor Nicolas II, during his visit to Vilnius on 11 November 1883.
Cotton, linen, 200 x 37.5 cm
Vilna, 1883
from: Vilna (?)

6802-87/ 1-2
Phylactery cases
Silver tefillin boxes with a flat base; a wide loop for belts. Decorated with engraving and the Star of David on the upper surfaces and floral designs on the sides; the letter 'shin' as part of the decoration.
Silver, hallmark: Tardy (1987), p.329; 4.5 x 7 cm
Poland, 1839
from: Western Ukraine, Volhynia/Podolia

A Jew wearing his phylacteries, Zinkovetsz, Podolia, 19th century

The synagogue of Ostropol

The synagogue of Nemirov, which was built on the ruins of the old excavated prayer house

Abraham Rechtman

The synagogue of Nemirov was famous for its outstanding architecture and unique construction. According to local tradition, this synagogue was erected with the help of the famous Graf Potozki, a lover of Israel and the lord of Nemirov. The Jews also relate this remarkable story.

Once a fire raged through the town and the monastery was completely gutted. The pious Graf Potozki promised the Christian population that he would build a new monastery.

For the convent's new site, he chose a hill in the middle of the town. All winter preparations continued: wood was assembled on the site, a mountain of bricks was collected, hundreds of peasants cut out poles and sawed the wood. Then, after Passover, the snow melted and the earth softened and the *Graf* sent workers to dig the foundations for the house.

But it happened that when the workers began digging they started to sink in the ground and it was only with great effort they were pulled out and saved. The next day, the workers went to dig in another corner. But the same thing happened, and so also on the third and forth day, when they tried other parts of the site. After listening to what had happened, the Graf ordered the work to be stopped.

The wise Graf realised that it could not be as simple as all that, and that the event was not accidental; on the contrary, there had to be another, deeper cause to explain the occurrence. So he started to ask among the town's old people, Jews and non-Jews alike, to read the old chronicles of the town and study old maps. Finally he reached his conclusion: the hill he had chosen for the new convent had been the site of a synagogue, destroyed by the Chmielnicki Cossacks in 1648.

This was a sacred place. It was wrong to try to build a convent on the site of a synagogue. His conscience troubled him; he became uneasy. He feared he had angered the Jewish God, and that this desecration would be revenged.

And so the story goes that on the second day of the feast of Shavuot, the Feast of Weeks (Pentacost), when the Jews were in the middle of reading the Book of Ruth in the great beth hamidrash, Graf Potozki suddenly arrived. He addressed the rabbi, sitting near the Aron Kodesh, the Holy Ark, and with a trembling voice related to the people around him what he had discovered about the hill. Raising his hand he swore that when he had decided to build the monastery there, he had had no idea that it had been the site of a Jewish synagogue.

Then Graf Potozki turned to the rabbi with tears in his eyes and asked the rabbi to pray for him and ask the Jewish God not to punish him for a crime he had committed unknowingly. As a proof of his sincere repentance, he promised to assist the Jews in building a synagogue precisely on that site, where the previous building had stood. He donated all the materials which had been assembled for the building of the convent for the construction of the new synagogue.

The rabbi calmed the Graf and looking at him with his bright eyes he explained that according to Jewish law no crime had been committed. He gave his word that he personally and all his congregation would pray to God for the Graf's health and well-being. So the Graf left the synagogue with his mind at ease.

And, indeed, after Shavuot the Jews started their sacred project. The rabbi dug the first hole and made the traditional 'shehechianu' blessing. Then all the congregation started work. That same day they excavated one of the walls of the old synagogue, and later when they reached the building's foundations they began with the construction of the new building.

The Graf used to appear regularly on the site to see how work was progressing. He provided all the necessary materials and gave orders to supply any additional needs. People came from far and wide for the opening ceremony. The Graf and his family were guests of honour. They were extremely happy.

I.M. Pulner Collection, 1931

6411-28/1,2
Torah scroll and mantle
A Torah scroll and mantle of red silk, for children
Paper, wood, silk, 10 cm
Byelorussia, 1900-1931
from: Byelorussia

6411-29
Chalizah sandal
A leather sandal made of 'pure' animal skin, with leather cords
(Yiddish: ghidn). This shoe was used purely for the chalizah, a
ceremony in which a childless widow removes the shoe from the
foot of her brother-in-law, in order to prevent him from marrying
her. In case he refuses this ceremony, she cannot remarry
somebody else.
Leather, 25 x 8 x 18.5 cm
Byelorussia, 1900-1920
from: Byelorussia

6411-31
Torah mantle
A miniature Torah mantle made of strips of silk, lilac-coloured
moire and ivory satin; decorated with a Star of David made from
metallic tape.
Silk, cotton, metallic galloon, 18 x 15 cm
Byelorussia, 1900-1920
from: Byelorussia

6411-33
Woman's wig
A wig made of natural hair, having long curls and a fringe.
Hair, 70 cm
Byelorussia, Lyady, 1900-1920
from: Byelorussia, Lyady

6411-34
Woman's wig
A wig made of natural hair, having two plaits and a fringe.
Hair, 45 cm
Byelorussia, Lyady, 1900-1920
from: Byelorussia, Lyady

Former Museum of Jewish Proletarian Culture, Odessa, via I.M. Pulner, 1936

6395-1
Shofar
Ram's horn, smoothed and polished, 19th century, decorated
with a longitudinal band and carving, the upper opening cut
in a wavy line.
Ram's horn, 40 x 7 x 4 cm
Western Ukraine, Volhynia/Podolia, 1800-1900
from: Odessa (?)

6395-8
Spicebox
A carved spicebox in the form of a tower, with a pointed top.
Ivory, 13 x 3 (diam.) cm
Western Ukraine, Volhynia/Podolia, 1800-1900
from: Western Ukraine, Volhynia/Podolia

6395-9
Matzah roller
A matzah roller (local name: matzah rigle) used when making
the dough for matzos. It consists of a piece of metal, folded double
with a small cogwheel between the two pieces.
Metal, 16.5 x 4.5 cm
Russia (?), 1880-1920
from: unknown

6395-12
Chanukah lamp
A China porcelain Chanukah lamp for oil with slightly curved
backplate decorated with three oval medallions with birds and
hunting scenes in the countryside.
China porcelain, 13 x 20 x 9 cm
Western Ukraine, Volhynia, Gorodnitsa, 1880-1920
from: unknown

6395-14
Book of Records
A minutes, or records book ('pinkas') with the following text on
the first page: 'This is the pinkas of the Mishna Study Society
form the Klaus synagogue of the Rabbi of Apta, of blessed
memory, from Medzhibozh, in the year (5)620 (1860)'. The
second illuminated title page contains for example the six tractates
of the Mishna and a slightly later date (5)624 (1864). The book
contains several decorated pages, surrounding the regulations of
the society and lists to commemorate the names of its members.
Parchment, 41 x 28 cm
Western Ukraine, Podolia, Medzhibozh, c. 1860
from: Western Ukraine

6395-18
Biscuit mould
A mould for biscuits in the shape of a fish produced in great
quantities by hardware manufacturers and individual designers
throughout Russia. This was a popular biscuit shape among Jews.
Tin-plate, 35 x 18.5 cm
Russia (?), 1880-1910
from: Ukraine

6395-19
Spicebox
A spicebox in a cylindrical form, decorated with engraved
hatching on a tall stem, with square base. The initials 'J.J.'
on the base have not been identified.
Silver, 20 x 4 (base) x 4 cm
Poland, 1800-1900
from: unknown

6395-23
Book of Records
A records book, or 'pinkas' from the charitable association 'Bikur
Holim'. The title page bears the words: Syaarei Tzedek (The gates
of justice) / Bikur Cholim (visiting the sick), Zhabokrich 1904.
Leather, paper, paint, 41 x 28 cm
Western Ukraine, Podolia, Zhabokrich, 1904
from: Western Ukraine, Podolia

The State Ukrainian Museum, Kiev, via I.M. Pulner, 1938

6413-1
Rug
A rectangular piece of textile probably used as a wall decoration in
the home, having a printed picture showing traditional Jewish and
Slavic motifs. These include a vase with flowers (in the centre)
surrounded by birds and deer. The vase of flowers is a stylized
variant on the eastern Slavic version of the Tree of Life. The
deer are a commonly-found Jewish motif.
Hemp, paint, 182 x 65 cm
Ukraine, 1900-1920
from: unknown

6413-7
Mizrach
A mizrach cut from white paper, pasted onto a piece of dark-blue
paper, with a floral and folk decoration including deer, birds and
flowers; at the top a crown and double-headed eagle; both top and
bottom have a Hebrew text: Mizrach [East] / From this side /
Spirit of life / When thou lightest the lamps, the seven lamps
shall give light over against the candlestick (Num. 8:2) in the
year (5)636 (1876).
Paper, Indian ink, 39.5 x 51 cm
Western Ukraine, 1876
from: Western Ukraine

Smiths, Polonnoye, 1914-16

Received from Segal, via I.M. Pulner, 1939

6405-2
Gingerbread mould
Biscuit mould in the shape of a doll (together with the biscuit 6406-32). This shape is typical of Russian gingerbread cutters in the 19th to 20th century.
Tin-plate, 2.2 x 12.5 x 4.7 cm
Russia, Ukraine, 1930-1939
from: Ukraine, Vinnitsa region, Bershad

6405-3
Gingerbread mould
Shape for gingerbread made of six extended containers having wavy rosettes at the end. This shape is typical for Russian gingerbread cutters in the 19th and 20th century.
Tin-plate, 2 x 12.5 x 4 cm
Russia, Ukraine, 1930-1939
from: Ukraine, Vinnitsa region, Bershad

6405-6
Gingerbread mould
Mould for gingerbread, diamond-shaped with wavy sides (together with biscuit 6406-50).
Tin-plate, 2.5 x 11 x 2.5 cm
Russia, Ukraine, 1930-1939
from: Ukraine, Vinnitsa region, Bershad

6405-7
Rattle
Tin-plate rattle, consisting of a long twisted piece with rotating part fixed in between the ends.
Tin-plate, 17 x 10 cm
Eastern Ukraine, Bershad, 1900-1940
from: Ukraine, Vinnitsa, Bershad

Museum of Jewish Proletarian Culture, Odessa, via I.M. Pulner, 1938

6402-1/1-32
Chessmen
A set for the game of chess, consisting of 32 pieces made of carved and painted wood. The figures have various Jewish attributes, such as the Star of David painted on a horse's head. Some are recognizable Jewish types, such as the rabbi or tzadik.
Wood, lacquer, 10.5 x 3.5 cm
Ukraine, Odessa, 1880-1920
from: Odessa

6402-2
Crossbow
A toy crossbow for children used during Purim.
Wood, paint, 29 x 7 cm
Ukraine, Odessa, 1930-1938
from: Ukraine, Odessa

6402-3
Rattle
A rattle, consisting of a wooden plate and hammer, used during Purim.
Wood, 26 x 22 x 7.5 cm
Ukraine, Odessa, 1930-1938
from: Ukraine, Odessa

6402-8
Gingerbread mould
A mould for gingerbread: rectangular with carved ornamentation on both sides showing a jug and a rhombus and leaves. The Hebrew letter 'shin' decorates the edge. The decoration on this baking shape is typical for Russian gingerbread moulds in the 19th-20th century.
Wood, 2.4 x 6.5 x 5.8 cm
Russia, Ukraine, 1900-1920
from: Ukraine

6402-9
Gingerbread mould
A square mould for gingerbread, with a carved geometrical pattern on one side, and the letter 'shin' on the rim. The decoration is typical of Russian wooden gingerbread moulds in the 19th-20th century.
Wood, 2.2 x 6.4 x 5.6 cm
Russia, Ukraine, 1880-1920
from: Ukraine

6402-10
Gingerbread mould
Triangular gingerbread mould with carved geometrical and floral decorations. Both technique and pattern are typical of the Russian wooden gingerbread moulds of the 19th-20th century.
Wood, 2.2 x 15 x 9 cm
Russia, Ukraine, 1880-1920
from: Ukraine, Odessa

6402-11
Gingerbread mould
Rectangular mould for gingerbread, with curving decoration in geometric and floral pattern.
Wood, 1.5 cm x 7.5 cm
Russia, Ukraine, 1880-1920
from: Ukraine, Odessa

6402-12
Gingerbread mould
A square mould for gingerbread, with carved floral rosette decoration. There is a Hebrew letter carved in the rim.
Wood, 2.3 cm x 6.4 cm x 5.4 cm
Russia, Ukraine, 1880-1920
from: Ukraine, Odessa

6402-13
Gingerbread mould
A diamond-shaped mould for gingerbread, with carved floral and geometric decoration, and a rosette at one side.
Wood, 1 x 12.5 x 5.2 cm
Russia, Ukraine, 1880-1920
from: Ukraine, Odessa

6402-14
Gingerbread mould
Fish-shaped mould for gingerbread, with the Hebrew letter 'shin' on the reverse.
Wood, 1.5 x 12.5 cm
Russia, Ukraine, 1880-1920
from: Ukraine, Odessa

S.B. Yudovin Collection, given to the museum in 1939

In 1939 S.B. Yudovin visited Beshenkovichi. Here he made a series of drawings of the characters who acted in a Purimshpiel [acted at Purim usually by travelling troupes] such as the wicked Haman, king Ahasveros, queen Vashti, Mordecai and his niece, queen Esther. In the traditional plays all these characters are acted by men.

6410-1
Costume sketch
Sketch for Haman.
Yudovin, S.B.
Paper, watercolour, 32.3 x 20.5 cm
Byelorussia, Beshenkovichi, 1939
from: Byelorussia, Beshenkovichi

6410-2
Costume sketch
Sketch for Ahasveros, king of Persia
Yudovin, S.B.
Paper, watercolour, 32.3 x 20.5 cm
Byelorussia, Beshenkovichi, 1939
from: Byelorussia, Beshenkovichi

The synagogue of Mihapol

The synagogue of Mirale in Brahilov

Abraham Rechtman

There are many shtetlech in Ukraine with synagogues bearing the names of pious women. And these women also have their legends and stories.

One such, which I shall relate now, is about the synagogue in Brahilov, told to me by old Yekutiel Segal, grandson of that pious genius, Rabbi Abraham Moshe Segal, rabbi of Brahilov and author of 'Holy Water'.

The Jews of Brahilov saved for years, cutting down on everything and putting aside kopek after kopek until there was enough money in the cash box to build a synagogue.

The whole congregation took part in the sacred work. Everyone laboured for months, assembling poles for the foundations, preparing cement and sawing wood. The construction work proceeded day by day, and as the building emerged so the happiness of the Jews of Brahilov grew. Adults and children – everyone helped, and everyone was happy.

Then one day – when the building was almost complete, and the Jews of Brahilov were full of pride in their beautiful building, with its splendid roof, higher than any other building in town and higher than the mountain outside town, shining like a mirror – an ill wind brought the Count back from some faraway place, presumably from over the ocean. He came back to his Brahilov castle, in the thick impenetrable forest.

The Count was a wicked, vicious man, an anti-Semite, who invariably got rid of any Jew unlucky enough to cross his path. And that evening, as the sun set in the west and its last rays shone through the synagogue windows, the angry Count drove into town. When he saw the new building, he was captured by its beauty and immediately decided to confiscate the synagogue from the Jews and turn this great, tall building into a monastery for the Goyim, the gentiles.

The following day the Count summoned the town elders, including the rabbi, and without a by-your-leave ordered the rabbi to surrender the new synagogue's keys. This was what he wanted and this was what he would have! If they refused, the Jews of Brahilov would suffer dearly. Then the Count turned and left.

The leaders returned like mourners from a funeral. The harsh decree broke everyone's heart. People cried and mourned for days. They pleaded with the Count, the rich landlords and the aristocrats tried to get him to reverse his decision. They begged him to show mercy to his faithful Jews and not take away their prayer house, their humble temple, which they had built with such sacrifice. But the Count was adamant and after a couple of days sent some of his servants to put a new lock on the synagogue door.

In Brahilov there lived a rich, aristocratic and pious woman, named Mirale, whose beauty was renowned. This Mirale took all her property and went to the Count's castle. She offered him all her gold, silver and jewels; and with tears in her eyes she asked the Count to show pity on her and her fellow Jews and repeal his harsh decree.

When the Count saw how beautiful she was, he fell in love with Mirale and became consumed by lust. So he said to her that he would be willing to accede to her request and cancel his decision if she slept with him that very night, but only that one night.

Mirale cried, and sobbing she fell at his feet asking him to take whatever he wanted of her property, but not to touch her. However, the Count had made up his mind he would reverse his decision, only if he could possess her body.

Realising that there was no way out and that she had no choice, Mirale told the Count that she would do as he wished. But she also had a condition. He must come to her in the middle of the night, and the keys to the synagogue door and permission to finish its construction should be given to her immediately.

The Count agreed, wrote his permission on paper, sealed it with his signet ring and gave the letter and keys to her. Mirale gave these to a messenger, who brought the wonderful news to the elders and to the jubilant inhabitants of Brahilov. The town celebrated its happy release.

The Count then locked Mirale in a room and posted a guard at the door.

Alone in that room, Mirale looked up to heaven and prayed to God with all her heart: 'Lord of the universe, since you put me to such a test, please, dear God, take my soul and place it together with all the other pure souls; take me unto you and prevent my body from being defiled by this terrible, vicious man. Help me, dear God, to remain pure as I am now.'

And she went on crying and praying, using all her spiritual powers, until her pure, untainted soul reached Heaven. And in the middle of the night, when the Count came to her room, he found her dead.

The Jews of Brahilov completed the building of the synagogue and named it 'Mirale's shul' after her.

6410-3
Costume sketch
Sketch for Vashti
Yudovin, S.B.
Paper, watercolour, 32.3 x 20.5 cm
Byelorussia, Beshenkovichi, 1939
from: Byelorussia, Beshenkovichi

6410-4
Costume sketch
Sketch for Vashti
Yudovin, S.B.
Paper, watercolour, 32.3 x 20.5 cm
Byelorussia, Beshenkovichi, 1939
from: Byelorussia, Beshenkovichi

6410-5
Costume sketch
Sketch for Mordecai
Yudovin, S.B.
Paper, watercolour, 32.3 x 20.5 cm
Byelorussia, Beshenkovichi, 1939
from: Byelorussia, Beshenkovichi

6410-6
Costume sketch
Sketch for 'Mondre jester' (?)
Yudovin, S.B.
Paper, watercolour, 32.3 x 20.5 cm
Byelorussia, Beshenkovichi, 1939
from: Byelorussia, Beshenkovichi

6410-7
Costume sketch
Sketch of a 'klezmer' with a fiddle
Yudovin, S.B.
Paper, watercolour, 32.3 x 20.5 cm
Byelorussia, Beshenkovichi, 1939
from: Byelorussia, Beshenkovichi

6410-8
Costume sketch
Sketch of a 'klezmer' with cymbals
Yudovin, S.B.
Paper, watercolour, 32.5 x 20.5 cm
Byelorussia, Beshenkovichi, 1939
from: Byelorussia, Beshenkovichi

6410-33
Bow
A child's bow for use during Purim.
Wood, paint, cotton cord, 42 x 12 cm
Byelorussia, Beshenkovichi, 1939
from: Byelorussia, Beshenkovichi

6410-35
Crossbow
A child's crossbow for use during Purim, painted red.
Wood, paint, 27 x 15 cm
Byelorussia, Beshenkovichi, 1939
from: Byelorussia, Beshenkovichi

6410-37
Chanukah spinning top
Spinning top (Yiddish: dreidl), with a small handle and faintly
outlined sections each bearing an inscription: A g[reat] m[iracle]
h[appened] t[here]. This top is used to play with during the
evening at Channukah. The text refers to the miracle of the oil
that continued burning in the lamp.
Tin-plate, 2.5 x 1.4 cm
Byelorussia, Beshenkovichi, 1930-1940
from: Byelorussia, Beshenkovichi

6410-38
Amulet
A piece of paper with a folk decoration and written text: Adam
and Eve, away with Lilith/Sanri/Sansavi/Semangelaf. This was
an amulet to provide protection against the evil demon Lilith,
for women in childbirth.
Paper, Indian ink, watercolour, 10.6 x 21.3 cm
Russia, Byelorussia, 1880-1910
from: Byelorussia, Beshenkovichi

6410-39
Amulet
A piece of paper with a floral decoration and a drawing of a boy
wearing a long upper garment and cap, with a written text: In
memory/ Adam and Eve/away with Lilith/Sanvi SanSanvi
Semangelaf/Shadai/Shmariel/Chasdiel. This was an amulet
to protect a woman and her newly-born son.
Paper, coloured ink, watercolour, 15.5 x 22 cm
Russia, Byelorussia, 1880-1920
from: Byelorussia, Beshenkovichi

6410-40
Amulet
A piece of parchment with text written inside a Star of David. The
text is a mixture of Isaiah 9:5 (for unto us a child is born) and the
words of the Nekhunia ben Gakana (?) prayer. This amulet was
used to ease the pains of labour and childbirth.
Parchment, Indian ink, 7 x 9.5 cm
Russia, Byelorussia, 1880-1920
from: Byelorussia, Beshenkovichi

6410-41
Amulet
A piece of parchment with a Star of David in the centre, and
written text. The word 'Jerusalem' in the centre of the star; above
the star the word 'litmubanim', composed from the first letters of
the first nine words in Exodus 23:26. Around this are the names of
God (Shadai) and the names of the archangels: Uriel, Michael,
Raphael, Gabriel with texts. This amulet was used to protect the
inhabitants of a house and their dwelling against evil.
Parchment, Indian ink, watercolour, 7 x 8.4 cm
Russia, Byelorussia, 1880-1920
from: Byelorussia, Beshenkovichi

6410-44
Sword
Toy wooden sword with carved painted handle, used by children
during the Purim festival.
Wood, paint, 43 x 3.5 cm
Byelorussia, Beshenkovichi, 1900-1920
from: Byelorussia, Beshenkovichi

The paperwork decorations listed below were made by Yudovin as
illustrations of the traditional Ukrainian paperwork that he
collected.

6412-33
Paper ornament
A white paper ornament (Yiddish: reyzele) made for the festival
of Shavuot, in the form of a rosette pasted onto grey paper.
Yudovin, S.B.
Paper, 59 x 49 cm
Western Ukraine, Podolia, 1900-1920
from: Western Ukraine, Podolia

6412-34
Paper ornament
A white paper ornament (Yiddish: reyzele) made for the festival
of Shavuot, pasted onto grey paper.
Yudovin, S.B.
Paper, 59 x 49 cm
Western Ukraine, Podolia, Voronovitsa, 1900-1920
from: Western Ukraine, Podolia, Voronovitsa

6412-37
Paper ornament
A white paper ornament (Yiddish: reyzele) made for the festival
of Shavuot, with a decoration showing a menorah, a two-headed
eagle and floral elements, pasted onto grey paper.
Yudovin, S.B.
Paper, 59 x 49 cm
Western Ukraine, Podolia, Voronovitsa, 1900-1920
from: Western Ukraine, Podolia, Voronovitsa

6412-38
Paper ornament
A paper cut-out ornament for the festival of Shavuot consisting of
a rectangular piece of grey paper with paper openwork decoration
pasted onto it, representing a menorah; a chain of Stars of David
form the edge.
Yudovin, S.B.
Paper, 59 x 49 cm
Western Ukraine, Podolia, Voronovitsa, 1910-1920
from: Western Ukraine, Podolia, Voronovitsa

Goldstein Collection, 1939

The following collection shows examples of different types of
bread, rolls, cakes and pies from the village of Bershad in the
Ukraine. In 1939 these local and traditional forms for bakery were
made from papier mâché and plaster. They were presented to the
State Ethnographic museum by Mr Goldstein.

6406-1
Pie, model
A dummy pie stuffed with honey-boiled pieces of dough. A
traditional local pie to be presented to a prospective bridegroom
by the fiancee's mother. Local name: a make der mamma.
Papier mâché, paint, 5 x 28 cm
Ukraine, Vinnitsa region, Bershad, 1939
from: Ukraine, Vinnitsa region, Bershad

6406-3
Challah, model
Sheaf-shaped bread used for sabbath; local name: khala.
Papier mâché, 6 x 26 x 18.5 cm
Ukraine, Vinnitsa region, Bershad, 1939
from: Ukraine, Vinnitsa region, Bershad

6406-4
Small cake or roll, model
A roll folded double, with a bird on top; local name: kitka.
Papier mâché, 6 x 21.5 x 17 cm
Ukraine, Vinnitsa region, Bershad, 1939
from: Ukraine, Vinnitsa region, Bershad

6406-5
Small cake, model
A small cake, or roll, in the shape of a diamond; local name: kitka.
Papier mâché, paint, 24 x 17 x 9 cm
Ukraine, Vinnitsa region, Bershad, 1939
from: Ukraine, Vinnitsa region, Bershad

6406-8
Challah, model
Oval challah loaf, made for sabbath.
Papier mâché, paint, 5.5 x 19.5 x 11 cm
Ukraine, Vinnitsa region, Bershad, 1939
from: Ukraine, Vinnitsa region, Bershad

6406-9
Challah, model
Round challah loaf, used for Rosh ha-Shanah.
Papier mâché, 6.5 x 12.5 cm
Ukraine, Vinnitsa region, Bershad, 1939
from: Ukraine, Vinnitsa region, Bershad

6406-10
Bread, model
A loaf of bread shaped like a ladder, used for Yom Kippur; local
name: loiter.
Papier mâché, 24 x 10.5 x 2.5 cm
Ukraine, Vinnitsa region, Bershad, 1939
from: Ukraine, Vinnitsa region, Bershad

6406-12
Challah, model
Bird-shaped challah bread, made for the sabbath; local name:
khala.
Papier mâché, 6 x 21.5 x 15.5 cm
Ukraine, Vinnitsa region, Bershad, 1939
from: Ukraine, Vinnitsa region, Bershad

6406-13
Challah, model
Bird-shaped challah bread made for sabbath; local name: khala.
Papier mâché, paint, 8.5 x 20 cm
Ukraine, Vinnitsa region, Bershad, 1939
from: Ukraine, Vinnitsa region, Bershad

6406-14
Challah, model
Bird-shaped challah made for sabbath; local name: khala.
Papier mâché, paint, 5.5 x 12.5 x 6.6 cm
Ukraine, Vinnitsa region, Bershad, 1939
site: Ukraine, Vinnitsa region, Bershad

6406-15
Challah, model
Oval-shaped challah made for sabbath; local name: khala.
Papier mâché, paint, 8 x 19.5 x 9.5 cm
Ukraine, Vinnitsa region, Bershad, 1939
from: Ukraine, Vinnitsa region, Bershad

6406-18
Roll, model
Oblong shaped bun.
Papier mâché, paint, 4 x 12.5 x 8 cm
Ukraine, Vinnitsa region, Bershad, 1939
from: Ukraine, Vinnitsa region, Bershad

6406-20
Roll, model
A small roll in the form of a figure eight.
Papier mâché, paint, 4.5 x 12 x 7.5 cm
Ukraine, Vinnitsa region, Bershad, 1939
from: Ukraine, Vinnitsa region, Bershad

6406-22
Roll, model
Round roll shaped like a rose.
Papier mâché, paint, 5 x 10 cm (diam.)
Ukraine, Vinnitsa region, Bershad, 1939
from: Ukraine, Vinnitsa region, Bershad

6406-24
Roll, model
A roll in the form of a young moon.
Papier mâché, paint, 3 x 13.5 x 10 cm
Ukraine, Vinnitsa region, Bershad, 1939
from: Ukraine, Vinnitsa region, Bershad

6406-26
Roll, model
An oblong bun.
Papier mâché, paint, 6 x 11 cm
Ukraine, Vinnitsa region, Bershad, 1939
from: Ukraine, Vinnitsa region, Bershad

6406-30
Roll, model
A rectangular bun.
Papier mâché, paint, 3 x 14.5 x 6 cm
Ukraine, Vinnitsa region, Bershad, 1939
from: Ukraine, Vinnitsa region, Bershad

A Jew with his sons, Lovich 1909

A group of women with a Polish girl, Lovich 1909

The Breslauer Kloiz in Dobne

Abraham Rechtman

The town of Dobne is surrounded by old oak forests, large orchards, streams and mills, wheat fields and gardens. All these belonged to *Graf* Lobomirski. The *Graf* had business connections with a Jew of Breslau, in Germany. This Jewish merchant was hired by the *Graf* to cut wood in his forests, serve as his orchard keeper, administer his mills and keep the streams in order. Thus the merchant spent most of his time in Dobne.

And soon the merchant came to the conclusion that instead of travelling backwards and forwards it would be better for him to settle in Dobne. So he built himself a beautiful house in the centre of town, brought his wife over – he had no children – and became a member of the local community. The man, considering himself an important figure, gave regularly to charity, provided the community's needs and, being a scholar, spent much of his time in the beth hamidrash, the Jewish house of study. Thus most of his contributions went to support the students.

The old beth hamidrash in Dobne was on the verge of collapse. Yet, although the roof had to be supported with struts and the walls were full of holes, still the place was always crowded with students and Torah scholars. The voice of the Torah was always heard there, day and night. The rich man talked to his wife and they came to the conclusion that they ought to build a new beth hamidrash since they had no children to support. This beth hamidrash would be the pride of the town and later, after a hundred and twenty years, it would still serve to commemorate their memories.

They got to work on their project straight away. They bought the best wood from the forests, baked beautiful brick stones and hired Jewish artisans. Everything was geared towards their sacred mission. They spared nothing and paid everyone more than their fair share. So, the new beth hamidrash rose up close to the old dilapidated building.

During the inauguration festivities, the rich man organized a big banquet, donated money for charity and was extremely satisfied with the final result. He had hired a carpenter, a real meister, who prepared the beautiful Aron Kodesh – the Holy Ark – and the book shelves. From Germany he imported chandeliers; and there were massive brass menorahs too. He provided the best and the most beautiful artifacts.

The rich man was elated and his wife was filled with happiness.

When all the ceremonies were over, the rich man approached the Jews learning in the old beth hamidrash and gave them the keys of the new building and said: 'Here, these are the keys of your new beth hamidrash. Come and learn Torah with pleasure. I would like to have the opportunity to be your servant'.

But the Torah students looked around, their eyes drifting away, and said: 'In our hearts we cannot accept your gift. We cannot leave our old building just like that. The walls and ceiling are permeated with our voices and they, the walls, will yearn after us. So as long as these old walls do not collapse, we shall remain here'. Ashamed, broken and miserable, the rich Jew went away. He and his wife could not be consoled. They cried bitter tears, with their new beth hamidrash deserted by day and unlit by night.

Some weeks passed and in his deep sorrow the rich man looked as if he had actually shrunk; his cheeks were hollow, his eyes dimmed and he walked around as if the weight of the world were on his shoulders. He was utterly helpless. Then, while in this state of misery, the Count summoned him. When the Count saw him and asked what had happened, the rich man was unable to contain his grief, he burst into tears and told the Count the whole story, from aleph to tav – from A to Z: how the scholars refused to leave their old collapsing beth hamidrash and accept a new, modern building, now standing empty and deserted.

The Count listened and said nothing. But that Friday, on the eve of sabbath when the Jews went to take their ritual bath, a score or more peasants showed up. Armed with axes and iron chains supplied by the Count, they took the old beth hamidrash to pieces, leaving it in ashes, and moved the Holy Ark and the Torah scrolls and other books to the rich man's new building.

When the Jews returned from the mikve, they saw what had happened and concluded simply that the rich man was trying to force them to move to his new beth hamidrash. So they turned their backs on the rich man and went to other communities in Dobne to learn Torah. When he saw what the Count had done, the rich man's sorrow was even greater. Fearing reprisals, he tried to convince people that this shameful deed had been done by the Count without his knowledge. He pleaded with the rabbi to show him mercy and spare him and his wife, and to help them clear their name.

That evening, when the sabbath was over, the rabbi convened a meeting and ordered the scholars of the old beth hamidrash to attend. The rich man addressed the congregation and repeated under oath that he had had

nothing to do with the crime; the Count had done it of his own accord. He asked the Torah students not to be stubborn and come and study in his new beth hamidrash. And yielding to the rabbi's persuasion, they eventually decided to follow his advice. They entered the new building, and the rich man and his wife were finally truly happy.

The rich man had a permanent place in the beth hamidrash, close to the door and among the poor. For the rest of his life he was glad to remain the humble servant of the scholars, and since then it has been known as the Breslauer Kloiz.

A beautiful wooden synagogue

A Jewish family

6406-32
Pastry, model
Sugar pastry, in the form of a human body, to be used during
Purim. Outlined with red stripes round the chest and hem; local
name: mentshele.
Plaster, wax, paint, 1.5 x 12 x 4 cm
Ukraine, Vinnitsa region, Bershad, 1939
from: Ukraine, Vinnitsa region, Bershad

6406-33
Pastry, model
Sugar pastry, shaped like a small horse, to be used during Purim.
Outlined with red paint, three red stripes along the body; local
name: aferdle.
Plaster, paint, 1.5 x 12 x 8.5 cm
Ukraine, Vinnitsa region, Bershad, 1939
from: Ukraine, Vinnitsa region, Bershad

6406-35
Pastry, model
A circular sweet pastry, to be used at Purim.
Plaster, wax, paint, 1.7 x 5.5 cm (diam.)
Ukraine, Vinnitsa region, Bershad, 1939
from: Ukraine, Vinnitsa region, Bershad

6406-45
Pastry, model
Sweet pastry with a tucked-in side, intended for Purim.
Plaster, wax, 1.8 x 4.5 x 5 cm
Ukraine, Vinnitsa region, Bershad, 1939
from: Ukraine, Vinnitsa region, Bershad

6406-49
Pastry, model
Oblong sweet pastry with ribbed edges, intended for Purim.
Plaster, wax, paint, 3 x 11 x 4 cm
Ukraine, Vinnitsa region, Bershad, 1939
from: Ukraine, Vinnitsa region, Bershad

6406-50
Pastry, model
Rhombic sweet pastry with ribbed edges, painted green and red,
to be used during Purim.
Plaster, wax, paint, 4 x 9 x 6 cm
Ukraine, Vinnitsa region, Bershad, 1939
from: Ukraine, Vinnitsa region, Bershad

6406-51
Pastry, model
A small pie shaped like a fish, intended for Purim; local name:
fluden, or fleddle.
Plaster, 4.5 x 18 x 8 cm
Ukraine, Vinnitsa region, Bershad, 1939
from: Ukraine, Vinnitsa region, Bershad

6406-52
Pastry, model
A rectangular pastry with decoration, to be used during Purim;
local name: fluden or fleddle.
Plaster, 2.7 x 7 x 5.5 cm
Ukraine, Vinnitsa region, Bershad, 1939
from: Ukraine, Vinnitsa region, Bershad

6406-54
Pastry, model
An oval pastry decorated with leaves on both sides, to be used
during Purim; local name: fluden or fleddle.
Plaster, wax, 6 x 4.7 x 2.5 cm
Ukraine, Vinnitsa region, Bershad, 1939
from: Ukraine, Vinnitsa region, Bershad

6406-63
Pastry, model
A triangular Hamantash pastry, intended for Purim; local name:
homentash.
Papier mâché, 13 cm
Ukraine, Vinnitsa region, Bershad, 1939
from: Ukraine, Vinnitsa region, Bershad

6406-76
Pastry, model
A rectangular pastry decorated with a picture of a jug; for use at
Purim; local name: lekach or lekechl.
Plaster, wax, 1 x 8.5 x 7 cm
Ukraine, Vinnitsa region, Bershad, 1939
from: Ukraine, Vinnitsa region, Bershad

6406-87
Pastry, model
A fish-shaped pastry, for use at Purim; local name: lekach, lekechl.
Plaster, wax, 1 x 14.2 cm
Ukraine, Vinnitsa region, Bershad, 1939
from: Ukraine, Vinnitsa region, Bershad

6406-92
Pastry, model
A rhombic-shaped pastry, decorated with a single rosette in the
centre, intended for Purim; local name: lekach, lekechl.
Plaster, wax, 1 x 14.5 x 6.5 cm
Ukraine, Vinnitsa region, Bershad, 1939
from: Ukraine, Vinnitsa region, Bershad

6406-100
Pastry, model
A triangular-shaped, decorated pastry, for use at Purim; local
name: lekechl, lekach.
Plaster, wax, 1 x 10 cm
Ukraine, Vinnitsa region, Bershad, 1939
from: Ukraine, Vinnitsa region, Bershad

6406-101
Pastry, model
An oblong-shaped pastry; local name: kitka.
Papier mâché, paint, 7 x 24 x 13 cm
Ukraine, Vinnitsa region, Bershad, 1939
from: Ukraine, Vinnitsa region, Bershad

6406-121
Pastry, model
A rhombic-shaped pastry with poppy seeds; local name: monelakh
or monelle.
Plaster, 8 x 7.5 x 3 cm
Ukraine, Vinnitsa region, Bershad, 1939
from: Ukraine, Vinnitsa region, Bershad

Former Museum of the Peoples of the USSR, Moscow, 1946

13058 'T'
Woman's blouse
A blouse of white machine-woven calico. The cut is straight
short, with gores; the upper opening is folded and fastened with
a button. Straight, wide sleeves, folded at the cuffs. This cut was
typical of the eastern Slavonic clothing for both men and women.
Printed calico, 57 x 65 x 55 (sleeves) cm
Russia, 1900-1920 (?)
from: unknown

13068 'T'
Man's belt
Black machine-woven woollen belt (Yiddish: gartle). It was
worn folded three times over the upper garment (kaftan) with ends
hidden. This belt is a typical garment for Jewish men round about
1900 in the western part of Russia.
Wool, 231 x 68 cm
Byelorussia, Mogilev Province, 1880-1920
from: unknown

The synagogue of Norinsk

The interiors of old synagogues

Abraham Rechtman

Interesting though the exteriors of old synagogues are, with their wonderful, individual architectural styles and their complex cornices, their interiors are infinitely more exciting: the patriarchal beauty, the richness and variations of colours, all these elements are immediately evident the moment you enter an old synagogue.

The first thing you notice is the ceiling: in the synagogue this is traditionally called the rakia – the sky or firmament – a custom based on the biblical verse from the beginning of Genesis: 'And God called the firmament Heaven'; for this reason it was customary to paint synagogue ceilings blue and decorate them with gold and silver stars. The decorations on the walls are equally striking and were drawn by anonymous artists with profound understanding and knowledge. But a unique range of utensils also catches the eye: the huge standing brass menorah's, the lamps and chandeliers suspended from the ceiling and the massive Chanukah lamps, made by coppersmiths of generations gone by. The ornaments carved on the arms of the menorahs and lamps include birds, animals, flowers and grapes. The centre-piece is of course the Aron Kodesh, the Holy Ark with its pillars, its wood carvings of lions and tigers, eagles and deer, reminiscent of Yehuda ben Tema's saying: 'Be as brave as a tiger, light as an eagle, quick as a deer and strong as a lion' [Avoth, cap. 5, mishna 20]. Then there are the velvet and silk parochets, and the caporet adorned with the Tablets of the Law, Aharon's hands and the names of the donators embroidered with gold and silver thread, as well as the Torah crowns, breastplates, pointers, and other sacred objects made by skilled artisans in silver and gold; the brass boxes for charity with verses engraved on them, copper basins, mezuzahs. All these articles have a modest, naive charm, and all of them have a unique, true and patriarchal beauty.

The ethnographic expedition managed to assemble a rich collection of these traditional objects as well as hundreds of photographs of synagogues and articles for the Jewish Ethnographic Museum.

Interior of the synagogue of Norinsk

**Illuminated page from the pinkas from the charitable society
'Righteous Shelter' in Baranovka**

What is a pinkas?

Abraham Rechtman

A pinkas is a book of records; it is the reflection of the life of a community or a society over the generations. It mirrors the emotions of its members: their happiness and sorrow, their pre-occupations and expectations. By examining pinkassim we can trace the lives of the individual members in great detail; we can study the communal customs and traditions of old, the relations between different groups of Jews and between Jews and the world of the Goyim.

The pinkas was a cherished, even a sacred object. People believed that fire would never break out and destroy a house where a pinkas was kept, and that women would never suffer complications in childbirth. Until recently it was the custom in many shtetlech to bring the pinkas into the house of a woman in labour and place it under her head to bring good luck.

Almost all the old pinkassim were written on parchment, or otherwise on very thick paper. All were bound in elegant leather, decorated with gold in the large Gemara (part of the Talmud) folio size; indeed, some were even bigger than Gemaras. The pinkassim were generally written in ketav sofrim (Hebrew square script); in some pinkassim, only the by-laws were written in ketav sofrim, while all other entries were in Hebrew cursive script. The pinkas title page and the first letter of each paragraph of the by-laws were often beautifully ornamented. In many cases the margins of the pages were decorated with intricate illustrations and beautifully varied colour combinations. Indeed, I am often amazed by the skill of our great-grandfathers, those students of the old-style beth hamidrash, those 'seat squeezers' as they're called in Yiddish.

Pinkassim in local societies

This type of pinkas can be found even in the most isolated of communities. Each town and shtetl of Ukraine usually had at least one pinkas; sometimes there were more than one, and sometimes even different types. Every shtetl had its own societies, and each society usually had its own pinkas.

The by-laws in this kind of pinkas are almost always the same in style as well as in content and terminology. These by-laws usually deal with the organisation of the society: the qualifications required of people applying to join, procedures for admitting new members and other matters such as registers of members, tax records, punishments, memorial days, allocation of alioth –

participation in the synagogue service on sabbath the election of functionaries and the duties of the individual within the society as well as the society's responsibilities towards its members.

According to some pinkassim elections were held in the society during Passover. The gabai, the head of the synagogue, could postpone elections if there were pressing reasons to do so and would fix another date later that year.

Elections could be held in various ways. In some societies the pinkassim relate how the members elected three to five representatives – 'borerim' – and these chose the functionaries. According to other pinkassim, the out-going functionaries chose the borerim. And in yet another group of pinkassim, the borerim were elected from among the out-going functionaries by all the members (kahal). Other pinkassim suggest that the borerim prepared a list (tzetl) of candidates, and the members chose a fixed number of officials from that list.

To be admitted as a member of a society was not easy. A candidate had to pass through several stages to qualify for entry and to become a full member of a society. But even after passing all the stages, it often happened that successful candidates had to wait years before being officially admitted, for there were only a limited number of places for new members. Indeed, some societies were so exclusive that they only allowed two new members a year. Many societies also forbade the admission of new members after 15 Kislev (roughly in mid-December). It is worth noting that some societies did admit children as a 'mitzva' – a meritorious or charitable act – but never more than two a year.

One should also point out that lamdanim – scholars – and in particular students of poskim, legal interpreters, were especially privileged in this respect. Their applications were not subject to the numerus fixus for new members, and they generally held a privileged position among the ordinary candidates during elections.

In the Medzhibozh pinkas the following regulation appears: 'If the vacancies for new members are filled and a person who has studied poskim applies to join, he will be admitted beside the others.'

An exception was also made in the case if a candidate was seriously ill, for admission might bring the applicant good luck. In such cases the gabai had the right to reject other candidates or demand that the number of vacancies be increased.

A carpenter, Annopol, 1914-16

Kehila pinkassim

The most important and valuable pinkassim are those of kehilas – communities. An examination of the contents of these pinkassim and a careful study of the events recorded in them, reveals a centuries-old history of organised Jewish communities, with the various aspects of communal life under careful regulation – internal affairs, relations between one community and another as well as matters connected with the world outside: the paritzim (local aristocrats) or the government.

The rabbis and local dignitaries took great care that the affairs of their community were conducted with respect and justice; ensuring that those in need of charity received it; being careful to be impartial; supervising schools and yeshivas (Talmud schools) and trying to provide assistance for poor students; taking particular care in the appointment of teachers and heads of yeshivas, always trying to get the best people; dismissing those who came under suspicion; settling disputes between individuals as well as societies; hearing witnesses and taking evidence under oath; regulating social affairs in order to prevent licence; appointing tax collectors to collect government taxes and take the census; lobbying on behalf of the community with central government and sending deputations to officials and local aristocrats; corresponding with other communities and working together with other kehilas for the general good; publishing pamphlets as well as fining and excommunicating people.
All this was meticulously recorded in the pinkas, and then signed by the rabbis and parnassim.

The pinkas as a chronicle

The pinkas was also a historical record. Everything that happened in the community was carefully recorded in the pinkas for future generations to read. If there was a plague, God forbid, and a person was commissioned to compose a prayer, both the event and the prayer would be recorded in the pinkas. If some extraordinary event occurred, or the state issued a decree which influenced community life in some way, a person would be asked to compose a lament or a poem and both the story of the event and the composition were copied into the pinkas. If a new fence was built round the cemetery, or a site for a new cemetery was surveyed, if new customs were introduced and regulations were passed and special prayers said in the synagogue – all these things would be entered into the pinkas, the chronicle of events for future generations.

Pinkassim also include stories about dybbuks, gilgulim (cabbalistic reincarnations), letzim (clowns), shedim (devils) and spirits; and there are stories about famous rabbis and healers, the 36 just men (the lamedvavniks). They include stories about freethinkers and desecrators of the sabbath traitors and criminals who were ex-communicated or thrown out of town, or people whose bodies were disinterred and buried near the cemetery wall – a 'donkey's burial'.
Pinkassim contain historical records about pogroms and persecutions, blood libels, anti-Jewish decrees by local aristocrats as well as miraculous deliveries and consolations. Most of the stories in the Ukrainian pinkassim are connected with the tragic events which occurred during two bloody episodes, that of Chmielnicki (1648/9) and Gonta's Haidamacks (1768).

The Haidamack massacres occurred some 120 years after Chmielnicki, and resulted in the destruction of hundreds of Jewish communities all over Ukraine. Evidence of these events is found in the pinkassim. There are lists of martyrs, special prayers commemorating the victims of the Haidamack leader Gonta, lamentations and chronicles describing the circumstances in which our great-grandfathers were martyred.

The widow, the daughter and Gonta's defeat

Among the hundreds of stories describing miracles which occurred at the time of Gonta, there are a number connected with his army's defeat and the general's own downfall.
I heard the following story from an old man in Brahilov, Reb Yekutiel Segal, a grandson of the famous, pious and learned Rabbi Abraham Moshe Segal, the author of 'Holy Water'. This book was printed in Mezeritch in 1790. Yekutiel and I were photographed on the porch of Yekutiel's house which had once belonged to his grandfather. Reb Yekutiel assured me that his father had written the story in the local pinkas, although this had been destroyed some years previously in a fire.

This is what the old man told me: When Gonta, cursed be his name, entered Brahilov, the first thing he did was ask where the tavern was. Whenever he entered a town he always let his soldiers get drunk before going on the warpath. He wanted his thugs to show no mercy so he let them drink as much as possible and let them start pillaging, plundering and robbing once they were thoroughly intoxicated.
At that time the tavern was run by a young widow assisted by her pretty daughter; the widow herself was a queen of beauty.
When Gonta saw the widow he immediately fell for her. He started softening her with sweet talk and after a couple of glasses of brandy he told her he loved her and wanted to marry her in accordance with the law. He promised her he would prepare a lavish wedding ceremony with a military parade, as befitted a Cossack leader.
The widow realised that she was in a serious predicament so she pretended to be overjoyed by his declaration of love and said that she would gladly accept his offer – but, she said, she had one condition. He must spare the town of Brahilov and ensure that nobody suffered at all. Gonta accepted her condition and gave strict orders

Jewish School (cheder) in Podolia, 19th century

that no-one should be harmed. He even stationed soldiers in the town to keep order.

In the middle of the night, Reb Yekutiel continued, a messenger arrived in town saying that the Poles were attacking nearby. Gonta and his men left town and went to fight the Polish army. Brahilov breathed again; God had delivered them. The widow, however, carried on crying and moaning. She realised that when the murderer returned, he would demand that she kept her promise; he would rape her and probably also her daughter. She was terrified at the thought of what was about to happen, so both mother and daughter, overcome by fear, decided to put an end to their lives rather than fall into Gonta's hands. They went down into the tavern basement and there the mother killed her daughter with her own hands and then took her own life.

The old man, Reb Yekutiel, remained silent. He was engrossed in his thoughts, trying to formulate the last part of the story. Then he resumed: Our God is Almighty, he punishes evil men according to their crimes! In that battle, Gonta, cursed be his name, and all his army were utterly defeated and so received a just punishment. Gonta himself suffered all kinds of terrible tortures; the Poles flayed him alive, cut through his flesh with a metal comb and finally they placed a red-hot metal crown on his head, mocking him as the new king of Poland.

The good news of Gonta's defeat spread like wild fire through all the Jewish communities of Ukraine. People prayed to God and thanked Him for this miraculous delivery. The news reached Brahilov the next day and the people were overjoyed. The whole congregation assembled in the great synagogue and sang the 'Hallel' psalms.

When people noticed that the widow is not present, the rabbi sent for her, and it was only then that the Jews found out what had happened to the mother and her daughter.

A deep sadness fell on the town. Everybody mourned and lamented the death of the widow; it was obvious to everyone: she had saved the Jews of Brahilov from certain death and in the end she had sacrificed herself and her daughter and had refused to fall into the hands of Gonta. The whole town brought the mother and daughter to the old cemetery with all the respect and honour due to them. And their story, as Reb Yekutiel told me, was written in the local pinkas.

Jewish children of two families, Podolia 19th century

13074 'T'
Man's headgear
A black velvet cap with a flap (kartuz). This type of man's hat was introduced into Jewish costume under the influence of tsarist government edicts of 1840 and 1850, which forbade Jews to wear clothes different from the Gentile population of the Empire. Velvet caps and lacquered peaks were popular among the 'raznochin' population during the second half of the 19th and the early 20th century.
Velvet, silk, wool, wadding, 7.5 cm x 17 (diam.) cm
Vilna Province, 1900-1920
from: unknown

13076 'T'
Skullcap
Man's headgear (Yiddish: yarmulka), made of 6 gores of black velvet, with green wool lining.
Velvet, wool, silk ribbon, 17 (diam.) cm
Byelorussia, Mogilev Province, 1880-1920
from: unknown

13083 'T'
Man's coat
A coat made of black cotton (kaftan). It has a straight skirt, with folds and inside pockets. Upright collar; sleeve cut straight. The coat is fastened with seven hooks. Collar, cuffs and skirt are edged with black velvet (known as 'Manchester'). This coat was worn with a belt. The cut, colour and manner of wearing were characteristic of the Lithuanian Jews' costume around 1900.
Velvet, cotton, calico, 139 x 115 cm; sleeves 64 cm
Vilna Province, 1880-1900
from: unknown

13090 'T'
Woman's blouse
Blouse of hand-made bleached linen (local name: geide). It is made from two lengths gathered at the yoke; straight collar, with long lapel, edged with narrow lace and tape. White calico sleeves with a gusset, gathered at the wrists and tied.
Linen, calico, 117 x 68 cm
Byelorussia, Mogilev-on-Dnjepr, 1900-1910
from: unknown

13096 'T'
Woman's jacket
A woman's sleeveless jacket, or waistcoat (local name: laptykanis), of red satin; it is close fitting, with turn down collar and three buttons. The collar and back are edged with narrow metallic galloon. This jacket is worn together with a bodice piece, or 'brustichel', no. 8763-13097 'T'.
Satin, cotton, braid with metallic threads, 35 x 34 cm
Ukraine, Kiev Province, Berdichev, 1880-1910
site: unknown

13097 'T'
Woman's bodice piece
A rectangular cardboard plate (Yiddish: brustichel), covered with red satin silk at the front and edged with metallic galloon. Calico, with a delicate flowered lining. Worn together with a jacket of the same fabric, no. 8763-13096 'T'.
Satin, printed calico, cardboard, metallic galloon, 51 x 13 cm
Ukraine, Kiev Province, Berdichev, 1880-1910
from: unknown

13099 'T'
Apron
An apron of printed calico (local name: farteh), with floral pattern (Russian factory production, late 19th-early 20th century). An apron was an essential element of Jewish women's clothing.
Printed calico, 84 x 78 cm
Ukraine, Kiev Province, Berdichev region, 1880-1920
from: unknown

13100 'T'
Apron
An beige-coloured apron of printed calico (local name: farteh) with large flowered design (Russian manufacture, late 19th-early 20th century). An apron was an essential element of Jewish women's clothing.
Printed calico, 88 x 101 cm
Byelorussia, Mogilev-on-Dnjepr, 1880-1920
from: unknown

13102 'T'
Woman's bonnet
A cap made of dark-grey calico, gathered at the back with a bodkin. Worn together with a kerchief.
Printed calico, 22 x 22 cm
Ukraine, Kiev Province, 1880-1900
from: unknown

13104 'T'
Woman's wig fillet
Woman's headgear, made from a rectangular strip of black silk.
Silk, calico, 48.5 cm x 14 cm
Byelorussia, Mogilev Province, 1900-1920
from: unknown

13107/1,2 'T'
Socks
One pair of knitted red and white cotton woman's socks (local name: zogny). The geometrical pattern is characteristic of Byelorussian-Lithuanian knitting. At the top there is an unidentified monogram (E3) and crown.
Cotton, 54 x 13 cm
Byelorussia, Mogilev-on-Dnjepr, 1900-1920
from: Byelorussia, Mogilev-on-Dnjepr

13108/1,2 'T'
Socks
One pair of knitted red cotton woman's socks (local name: zogny). They is have a design of fish, flowers and geometrical figures, together with an unidentified monogram (E3).
Cotton, 39 x 14 cm
Byelorussia, Mogilev-on-Dnjepr, 1900-1920
from: Byelorussia, Mogilev-on-Dnjepr

13110/1-2 'T'
Woman's shoes
A pair of shoes, without counter (piece at the back of the heel); made of brown leather (local name: pantefl). Solid sole, brown leather insole. Typical for shoes of both Jewish men and women, worn in southwest Russia in the 19th century.
Leather, 25.5 x 7.5 cm
Kiev Province, 1880-1900
from: Kiev Province

13111/1-2
Woman's shoes
A pair of shoes, with a low heel, without counter (piece at the back of the heel); made of brown leather (local name: pantefl). White kid insole. Characteristic of the type of shoes worn by Jews in southwest Russia in the 19th century.
Leather, 24 x 7.5 cm
Mogilev Province, 1880-1900
from: Kiev region

13112/1-2
Woman's shoes
A pair of shoes, with low heels, piping, pointed toes, without counters (piece at back of heel) (local name: pantefl). Brown leather insole. Backless shoes were typical for the Jewish population of southwest Russia in the 19th century.
Leather, 23 x 8 cm
Mogilev Province, 1880-1900
from: unknown

13114 'T'
Woman's necklace
Four strands of artificial pearls (local name: pirl) of varying size,
with blue silk tapes for tying. Worn by women together with
8763-13096 'T' and 8763-13097 'T').
Glass, silk, 77 cm
Kiev Province, 1880-1900
from: unknown

13140 'T'
Woman's skirt
A skirt of dark-blue satin, broad pink printed calico panel with
floral design at the front (local name: flyidr). The skirt is of four
pieces, gathered at the top with narrow edging; black tape edging
at hem. Fastened with one hook; grey calico lining. Worn together
with 8763-13096 'T' and 8763-13097 'T'.
Satin, printed calico, metal, 96 x 110 cm
Kiev province, Berdichev, 1880-1900
from: unknown

13265 'T'
Woman's sleeveless jacket
A woman's sleeveless jacket, or waistcoat, of black ornamented
silk. It has a straight cut, loose back and turn-down collar; two
silk-covered buttons at the front; the collar and left opening are
edged with metallic galloon. There are three grey calico fasteners
for attaching a skirt.
Silk, calico, metallic galloon, 33 x 40 cm
Byelorussia, Mogilev-on-Dnjepr, 1880-1920
from: unknown

13266 'T'
Woman's sleeveless jacket
A waistcoat of black semi-wool, with green striped textile. It has a
straight front, loose back; large round turn-down collar; two silk-
covered buttons on the left-hand side; the collar and the edges are
finished with metallic galloon. There are three black calico
fasteners for attaching a skirt
Flax, lasting, metallic galloon, 35 x 44 cm
Byelorussia, Mogilev-on-Dnjepr, 1880-1920
from: unknown

Former Museum of the Peoples of the USSR, Moscow and Former Polytechnical Museum collection

13125 'T'
Prayer shawl
A prayer shawl made from a rectangular piece of white fustian,
edged with black lasting (a strong closely-woven fabric) strips
and black cord, with 'atora' metallic galloon fringe at the corners.
Made in home conditions from available materials. This prayer
shawl is a fine example of 'making do with what one had' – unable
to weave the stripes into the fabric, the makers have sewn them
onto the cloth.
Cotton, metallic galloon, 183 x 192 cm
Eastern Europe, 1880-1910
from: unknown

13126 'T'
Torah ark curtain
A Torah curtain of machine-made dark-blue and red striped
textile with a decoration of a Star of David and fringe. See also
8762-13129 'T'.
Wool, gauze, metallic galloon, metal, 93 x 58 cm
Eastern Europe, 1880-1920
from: unknown

13128 'T'
Tallit katan
A tunic-shaped garment made from crimson textile, with brown
and white stripes, and tzitzit – tassels – at the corners.
Cotton, 65 x 31 cm
Eastern Europe, 1880-1920
from: unknown

**A portrait of a Jew from Vilna, wearing his prayer shawl,
19th century**

13129 'T'
Torah ark valance
A valance made of dark-blue and red striped machine-made textile with a decoration of a Star of David and fringe. (See also no. 8763-13126 'T').
Wool, metal braid, 62 x 35 cm
Eastern Europe, 1880-1920
from: unknown

13132 'T'
Prayer shawl
A prayer shawl of white and black wool, decorated with a neckpiece of brocade ('shpanyer'), and with tzitzit at the corners.
Wool, metallic thread, silk, 160 x 0.90 cm
Eastern Europe, 1880-1900 (?)
from: unknown

13134 'T'
Tallit katan
A tunic-shaped garment made from printed calico, with stripes of lilac colour. Vertical collar; unsown left shoulder seam, fastened with tapes and tzitzit at the corners.
Printed calico, 98 x 45 cm
Eastern Europe, 1850-1900 (?)
from: unknown

Former Museum of the Peoples of the USSR, Moscow
I.M. Pulner Collection, 1930

13084 'T'
Man's coat
Men's outdoor garment resembling a kaftan (local name: kapota), of black woollen fabric. It is cut in one piece with a wide flared skirt; turn-down collar; long wide sleeves. Black calico lining. Worn with a belt. The cut, colour and manner of wearing was typical of the Latvian and Byelorussian Jews of the late 19th to early 20th century.
Wool, calico, 137 x 127 cm; sleeves: 64 cm
Byelorussia, 1900-1920
from: Byelorussia

13087 'T'
Man's coat
Man's outdoor garment resembling a kaftan (local name: tyzlyk), made from dark-grey cotton lasting. Cut with a straight wide skirt, fitting at the waist back, with folds and pockets in the side seams; buttons at the waist; straight collar; long straight sleeves, fastened with 32 hooks. The edges decorated with black velvet (so-called manchester). Dark-grey calico lining. Worn with a belt. The cut and manner of wearing were characteristic of the Byelorussian Jews of the 19th to early 20th century.
Cotton, calico, wadding, velvet, 141 cm
Byelorussia, 1900-1920
from: Byelorussia

13088 'T'
Man's coat
Coat made of dark-grey lasting. A straight wide skirt; seam at back; turn-down collar; straight sleeves, finished with black velvet (so-called manchester) stripe. Grey calico lining. Worn with a belt. The cut and manner of wearing were typical for the Byelorussian Jews of the late 19th to early 20th century.
Cotton lasting, calico, velvet, wadding, 138 cm
Byelorussia, 1900-1920
from: Byelorussia

13106/1,2
Socks
One pair of knitted grey cotton woman's socks (local name: zogny).
Cotton, 38 x 14 cm
Byelorussia, Vitebsk Province, 1920-1930
from: Byelorussia, Vitebsk Province

Two Jewish men with caps (kartuz); the person on the right wears a 'capote' type coat

An elderly Jew, Lovich 1909

Amulet to protect a woman and her newly-born son
6410-39

Healers, magicians and fortune-tellers

Abraham Rechtman

Priceless charms and amulets

As with the Talmud story in Berachot 20 about Rabbi Yohanan and the evil-eye, the Gemara contains many references to this subject. This particular story is important for two reasons: firstly, it shows that such beliefs were widespread in Talmudic times, and perhaps even in earlier periods; secondly, it mentions Joseph the righteous, quoting verses from the Bible and showing that Joseph and his sons were immune from the evil-eye. In the stories that follow, Joseph appears regularly. According to the Talmud the evil-eye is in reality a disease with the property of itself causing other illnesses. Thus the Talmud discusses medicines against this disease, remedies to counter its effects and ways to prevent the spread of diseases connected with the evil-eye.

The belief in the good and evil-eye and in remedies is therefore an ancient belief and has continued to exist throughout the generations. Travelling through the towns and shtetlech of Ukraine, the ethnographic expedition tried to find out more about how deep this belief really went, how widespread it was and how many healers and fortune tellers had inherited these skills from previous generations.

Almost every shtetl in Ukraine had its old women whom people went to for advice in times of crisis. Pregnant women – especially when carrying their first child – often asked these older women for protection. People believed not only that they had the power to predict an unborn baby's gender but that they could in fact influence whether it would be a boy or a girl. Those old ladies had a supply of 'proven' charms and spells for each occasion: for acquiring a good-eye, for toothache, a bad foot, an abscess, a 'rose' (inflammation of the skin), the bite of a dog, epilepsy and other maladies; these women performed magic with knives, socks and combs; they poured wax and poached eggs and knew hundreds of ways to cure a patient.

It was tremendously difficult to collect this kind of material and it took a lot of effort. The old women were very careful not to divulge their secret spells and remedies to others; they even refused to tell members of their own family. They seem to have felt that if they revealed a spell or a secret remedy to anybody else they would be giving up part of their powers and so would inevitably become weaker. Moreover, being guilty of a sort of treachery they would themselves suffer some form of retribution if they ever used those spells or medicines again.

We employed various strategies to get these old women to tell us their charms. Sometimes one of us would pretend to be ill, take to bed and call for the healer. Approaching the patient, she would pour wax, murmur and call on the good-eye, etc. Another member of the expedition generally sat in a corner, trying to write down everything he heard while the photographer took pictures.

Often An-sky would go to one of these old healers and complain that he was suffering continual bad luck; he told them that he had once been a rich man, a merchant, and now – alas – he was poor, fallen on hard times, without an income. And having explained why he had come to ask her for help he would ask her to give him some magic spells to help him find a way to earn a living. An-sky was always careful to mention that he was not looking for charity but ready to pay for her services. His broken voice and his straight-forward story nearly always produced the desired result. The old woman would get caught up in the story and start to pity her client, hoping later to be able to ask more money. Having haggled over the price the old woman would reveal her secret spell and An-sky would write it down.

One day I joined in just such a session. We claimed that An-sky was unable to write and was almost blind, he took me along as a scribe. And I remember that when we left the old lady blessed An-sky and promised him that God would be generous in giving him what he was looking for.

Women's charm amulets

To give you a better idea about these spells and remedies, I have selected some examples which deal with the evil-eye and some other maladies. These spells are recited in Yiddish and Ukrainian, and I will try to describe how the women acted during the performance of the spell. The following popular spell is against the evil-eye:
Three women are seated on a stone. One says that [so and so] has an evil-eye; the second says, no; the third says that it must return to where it came from. If a man has wronged that person, he will lose his beard, and if it is a woman who wronged the subject, she will lose her teeth and breasts. There is no sea route, the fish have no kidneys and you will not possess an evil-eye and no malady will afflict you. These three women will guard and toil for you and provide you with good and ensure that you be healed from your malady and be safe as certainly as God healed Hizkiahu. Tfu, tfu, tfu (spit three times and sneeze).
[Chaiah Beile Shapira, Alt-Konstantin]

It is indeed remarkable and astonishing that despite living in isolated communities, having no contact with the outside – Goyish – world and looking down on the Goy's belief in *Joizl* (Jesus), the mass of orthodox Jews were quite familiar with gentile folklore: their spells, remedies, charms and magic. Jews often went to gentile healers and might even take sick people to faraway places to see such a healer. In some cases, a messenger would be sent to the healer to receive a blessing, or the healer might bless the sick person's shirt or a child's blanket. They would then wear the garment until they recovered.

Another short charm for a good-eye was revealed to me by Chaiah Tverski. All the family and household are gathered together; they all stand in a circle around the sickbed and hold hands, while the oldest person in the room says: '[So and so] has the evil-eye', and everyone replies: 'Oi-vei, oi-vei, oi-vei, a sin!'. This is repeated ten times and later everybody yawns.

The preparations for the performance and the way in which the spell is executed can be different: the women make a noise, wink, pinch their noses and blow; some even bark like dogs, crawl on all fours, bleat like sheep, go round in circles or hop around the bed. They also use utensils such as knives, combs, soap, sackcloth and often use a wagon wheel.
Before starting the woman washes her hands seven times. After each time, she puts her hands on the sick person's head; after the seventh time she continues holding the patient's head until she has completed the treatment. Then, she licks the person's forehead seven times; each time spitting against the wall. Later, she dips her fingers in the patient's saliva or urine and wets the patient's forehead with it.

A woman of Letichev, named Genendl, was known throughout the region for her charm amulets. When we came there and heard about her fame, we pulled straws and I was chosen to play the sick man and lie in bed. We sent a messenger, a prominent local Jew, asking her to come to see me. It was an achievement in itself to have got her to come at all since she never accepted money from anyone and she was very old, being barely able to stand. She belonged to a respected family of rabbis and righteous men, so she did what she did for charity. The messenger told her that I was an important man, a rabbi's son and a brilliant rabbinical student. I was a guest in town, had come for charity, and had suddenly fallen ill. So she came to see me.
The first thing she did was order everyone to leave the room. Alone with her patient she filled the room with incense she had brought with her. Then she asked me to give her my vest. Holding this she began to murmur and grimace; then she wiped my forehead with the cloth and laid it under my head. Then she produced a pen-knife, passed it over the incense and placed it under my pillow. Next she began to wash her hands. She washed seven times and between each time she did all kinds of things, not resting for a moment. She broke boxes, pulled my hair, lay on top of me uttering inexplicable

words. To this day I still cannot imagine how I managed to endure the whole procedure – it went on and on and forever...
When she had finished these endless spells, she drew the penknife from under the pillow and cut the nails on my left hand – the hand on which you wind the tefillin (phylactery) strap. She put the pieces of nail in a piece of bread and placed this in my hands, telling me to feed this to a male black dog (not a bitch – that would only help women!). This ceremony of cutting the nails with this penknife, putting it in bread and giving it to a black dog was to be repeated three consecutive days. Then she gave me back my vest, which I also had to wear for the next three days.

Men's charm amulets

The secret knowledge of spells, remedies and other charm amulets was not restricted to women. In many towns and shtetlech throughout Ukraine, there were old men who proved to be as specialised as the women. They had spells and remedies for every conceivable problem. Yet people always seemed to trust the women more than the men and so men were less frequently approached.
Men's spells differ from those of women in one major respect: language. Women used Yiddish and Ukrainian, or both at the same time, while men stuck almost exclusively to the holy tongue. They generally used biblical Hebrew, but they would also use the language of the Zohar (central Kabbalistic work). These men gained their knowledge from old manuscripts and rare books, which had been handed down from generation to generation.

In Drazne I saw manuscripts of charm amulets, spells, remedies and oaths in the house of the Talmud teacher, Rabbi Yisrael Shreibman. He assured me that the book had belonged to his pious ancestors and that the spells, remedies and oaths were all proven. Indeed, he was famed as a healer throughout the region, and people came to consult him from shtetlech far and wide...
The interesting short spells found in his manuscripts include one for when faced by a dog: in such an event what you should say is, 'Dog, dog, I am the son of Jacob. You are Esau's dog. If you bite me, foxes will tear you apart.' A remedy for fever (kadoches):

Find a live black spider; the live spider should be put into the split casing of a nut. This should then be resealed using pitch or wax and made to look like an unopened nut. Cover the nut containing the spider with cotton cloth; sew it closed with black thread; the patient should wear the nut and spider around the neck for seven days.

I found all kinds of fantastic spells and remedies in this man's manuscripts for any number of illnesses, possible and impossible, real and unreal, natural and unnatural as well as for a whole variety of other problems.

Еврей 40 лѣтъ.

13121
Tablecloth for sabbath
A tablecloth, used during sabbath, with a wide strip of hem-stitch decoration down the sides and centre, edged with wide frill.
Cotton, 118 x 118 cm
Mogilev Province, 1900-1910
from: Mogilev Province

4847 'D'
Saucepan
A saucepan with a flat handle.
Tin-plated brass, 12 x 38 x 21 (diam.) cm
Byelorussia, 1900-1920
from: Byelorussia

4848 'D'/a,b
Saucepan
A saucepan with a lid and two handles, for cooking stuffed fish.
Tin-plated brass, 64 x 18 x 19 cm
Byelorussia, 1900-1920
from: Byelorussia

4849 'D'
Grater
A flat tin-plate grater for horseradish, with a curved wire handle.
Tin-plate, 20.5 x 8.8 cm
Byelorussia, 1900-1920
from: Byelorussia

4853 'D'
Saltcellar
A wooden carved and decorated saltcellar in the form of a square box, with a high back. The decorations consist of a Star of David at the front, a single rosette on left side and a lion and unicorn on the right side. The back shows houses, hunters, an eagle, a wolf and a dog. The side rims present human and animal shapes in relief. On the reverse is a human figure within a crown. The figures are accompanied by inscriptions: Eat a morsel with salt. A house, a hunter, an eagle, a wolf, a dog.
Wood, 19 x 11 x 11 cm
Byelorussia, 1900-1920
from: Byelorussia

4860 'D'
Washing block
A rectangular washing block with a short round handle; widely used among the folk population of Russia.
Wood, 33 x 13 x 7.5 cm
Byelorussia, 1900-1920
from: Byelorussia

4867 'D'
Chanukah lamp
A Chanukah lamp, made by local craftsmen, having a backplate with stamped geometrical decorations and an oil container with eight pans.
Zinc-coated tin-plate, 15 x 23.5 x 3.7 cm
Byelorussia, 1900-1930
from: Byelorussia

4870 'D'
Rattle
A wooden rattle, used during Purim.
Wood, print, 16 x 20 x 6.5 cm
Byelorussia, 1900-1920
from: Byelorussia

4871 'D'
Rattle
A wooden rattle, with inscription: 'Aman', used during Purim.
Wood, 18 x 15.5 cm x 7.5 cm
Byelorussia, 1900-1920
from: Byelorussia

4872 'D'
Rattle
A long wooden rattle (local name: grager). Used during Purim.
Wood, 7 x 25.5 x 18.5 cm
Byelorussia, 1900-1920
from: Byelorussia

4873 'D'
Rattle
A wooden rattle used during Purim.
Wood, 6 x 24 x 19 cm
Byelorussia, 1900-1920
from: Byelorussia

4874 'D'
Rattle
A wooden rattle of rectangular plywood plates, and connected with string. Used during Purim.
Wood, 15.5 x 10 cm
Byelorussia, 1900-1920
from: Byelorussia

4875 'D'
Rattle
A rattle made of tin, used during Purim.
Tin-plate, 16 x 17 x 2 cm
Byelorussia, 1900-1920
from: Byelorussia

4887 'D'
Alms box
A rectangular box of painted metal with an opening on the side; on the lid and the bottom is a Hebrew text painted in white: Charity saves from death (Proverbs 10:2).
The text refers to the way in which this box was used to collect money for the charitable association that arranged burials and everything connected with a funeral.
Tin-plate, paint, 3.5 x 8.5 x 6 cm
Byelorussia, 1900-1920
from: Byelorussia

4891'D'
Ram's horn
A ram's horn, or shofar, with an opening on both sides, the upper one edged with a narrow metal strip.
Ram's horn, 49 x 8 x 3.7 cm
Byelorussia, 1900-1920
from: Byelorussia

4895 'D'
Seder plate
An earthenware seder plate with illustrations and Hebrew texts, relating to the 15 parts of the order of the Passover meal on the rim and in the centre the names of the six symbolic foods.
F. Zusman factory
Glazed earthenware, paint, 2 x 23 (diam.) cm
Ukraine, Volhynia, Kamennyi Brod, 1900-1920
from: Byelorussia

4896 'D'
Chanukah spinning top
A cone-shaped spinning top (local name: dreydl), with a stem and Hebrew letters: A g[reat] m[iracle] h[appened] t[here]. The Hebrew letters refer to the miracle of the oil that continued burning in the lamp.
Tin, 2.5 x 1.4 cm
Byelorussia, 1900-1920
from: Byelorussia

4901 'D'
Bread mould
An oval mould for baking bread.
Tin plate, 8 x 14 x 23 cm
Byelorussia, 1900-1920
from: Byelorussia

4995 'D'
Trough
An oval trough with flat rectangular handles, for chopping meat.
Wood, 7 x 47 x 22 cm
Byelorussia, 1900-1920
from: Byelorussia

A shoemaker, Kreshenetsz, 1914-16

Incidental gifts

Acquired from M. Sverdlov, 1910

1688-1
Woman's jacket
A woman's sleeveless jacket, or waistcoat, made of brocade with floral pattern. A fitted waist. Turn-down collar, the left flap edged with brown silk and collar and lapels edged with metallic galloon. The buttons are covered with yellow silk threads. Calico lining.
Gold brocade, calico, metallic thread, 21 x 29 cm
Byelorussia, Mogilev-on-Dnjepr, 1880-1900
from: unknown

Acquired from B.M. Ad. Veselovskaya-Shanyavskaya, 1911

1980-1
Woman's jacket
A woman's sleeveless jacket, or waistcoat, made from 'slutsk' silk, with metallic thread. The back cut straight, sides and front with tucks. High turn-down collar. Metallic-cord buttons, the one on the upper left being covered with 'slutsk' silk. White calico lining.
Calico, damask ('slutsk' silk), 30 x 40 cm
Western Ukraine, 1880-1900
from: unknown

1980-2
Woman's bonnet
A woman's festive cap made of old damask (Western Europe, 18th century), with floral pattern, on white fustian lining. Worn together with a wig and a head-kerchief.
Silk, metallic thread, fustian, 22 cm
Western Ukraine, 1880-1910
from: unknown

Acquired from F.M. Plushkin, 1914

3235-6
Chanukah lamp
A 'Baal Shem Tov' filigree Chanukah lamp (so called after the name of the founder of Chassidism). The backplate is decorated on both sides with columns and vases with flowers; a door in the centre, with a large filigree rosette above (architectural 'rose'); a crown with a candlestick at the top.
Silver, hallmark: Tardy (1987), p.328; 16.5 x 20 cm
Poland, Cracow, 1847
from: western part of Russia

3235-14 a,b
Spicebox
A spicebox in the form of a scent bottle, with removable bottom.
Silver, 4.7 x 2.5 (diam.) cm
Europe (?), 1700-1800
from: western part of Russia

Acquired from A.I. Novodvorski, 1911

2198-1/1,2
Candlesticks
One pair of sabbath candlesticks
Silver-plated brass, 23.5 x 12 cm
Russia, 1800-1900
from: North-West Russia

Acquired from A.I. Novodvorski, 1923

4056-1
Chanukah lamp
A Chanukah lamp for oil, the backplate with an openwork lattice, and a crown and two snake heads at the top. The side panels are decorated with diamond-shaped lattice and birds. The animal motifs are characteristic of the work of Ukrainian and Polish brass craftsmen in the 18th-19th century.
Brass, 27 x 26 x 13.5 cm
Poland, 1775-1800
from: European part of Russia (?)

Acquired form E.S. Raize, 1923

7851-25
Cap
A velvet cap with a flap; local name: kartuz
Velvet, 17 (diam.) x 7 cm
1900-1930
from: Byelorussia

Acquired from Vemrik, 1932

6404-1 /1-32
Chanukah playing cards
A set of 32 handmade Chanukkah playing cards; on each card a letter of the alphabet and a floral decoration; 12 cards are decorated with signs of the zodiac.
Paper, watercolour, 9.2 x 6 cm
Ukraine, Odessa, 1900-1920
from: Ukraine, Odessa

Acquired from 'klezmer' Rabinovich, Odessa, 1938

6408-4a/b, 6a/b, 7a/b, 8, 9, 11, 12a/b
Musical instruments
A set of musical instrument used by klezmers. Klezmers, or folk musicians, played in the 'Purim shpils' and were invited to play at weddings and festivals. The set of instruments consists of: violoncello, flute (length 73.4 cm), cymbals (diam. 28 cm), trombone (length 113, inscribed: E.I. Schmidt [W]eimar), cornet (39 x 18 cm, inscribed: Imper[ial] Priv[ate] Mus[ical] Factory of Shediva Odessa. Hallmark: I.T.C.B. 1894, no24), drum (29 x 52 (diam.) cm), violin (60 x 20.5 cm, restored in the 19th century, the back bearing a maker's label; the top piece of the violin is late 19th century).

Acquired from E. Rudman, 1939

6407-1
Passover cup
A transparent glass passover cup with a stamped floral decoration and cartouche with a Hebrew text: Passover.
Glass, 8 x 5.5 cm (diam.)
Eastern Ukraine, Vinnitsa region, Bershad, 1900-1920
from: Eastern Ukraine, Vinnitsa region, Bershad

6407-2 / 1-17
Chanukah playing cards
A set of 17 Chanukah playing cards with Hebrew letters; the cards are numbered from alef (1) to lamed (32), some have a Hebrew text: nr. 31: I give money; nr. 32: Give me money; nr. 21: Ephraim
Paper, ink, 9.9 x 8.5 cm
Ukraine, 1900-1920
from: Ukraine

Klezmerband, 1910-1914

Jews of Vilna region, 19th century

A Jew standing at the sledge, Radin 1909

6407-9
Gingerbread mould
A fish-shaped biscuit shape, with carved decoration on both sides.
Wood, 2 x 21.5 x 9.5 cm
Ukraine, Vinnitsa region, Bershad, 1930-1939
from: Ukraine, Vinnitsa region, Bershad

Acquired from P.Sh. Zaltsman, 1941

6427-1
Book of Records
Minutes book or 'pinkas' with 23 pages of notes and four pages of handwritten text. From the charitable society 'Righteous Shelter' in Baranovka.
Paper, leather, 35 x 23.5 cm
Western Ukraine, Volhynia, Baranovka, 1880-1900
from: Western Ukraine, Volhynia, Baranovka

Acquired from S.I. Vygodskaya-Frid, 1957

6987-1
Etrog box
A rectangular box on four legs, with a lid and matt engraved surface, decorated with a cartouche in the shape of a shield, with monogram and floral frieze.
Silver-plated brass, hallmark: oval shape with central 'W' letter edged with the words Hendelsman Warszawe; 8.5 x 13 x 9.5 cm
Poland, 1900-1920
from: unknown

Acquired from E.S. Raize, 1969

7851-4
Cooking pot
A cooking pot with one handle. The shape of this pot is typical for the cooking utensils used on Russian stoves in the 19th and 20th century.
Tin-plated brass, 17 x 18 (diam.) cm
Russia, 1900-1920
from: unknown

7851-11
Passover cup
Passover cup, made of blue glass, with white decoration and inscription: Passover.
Glass, 7.5 x 5 (diam.) cm
Russia, 1900-1920
from: unknown

7851-23
Man's coat
Festive man's garment, of black fabric with black cotton lining; local name: capota. Long, shaped back; long sleeves; black silk lapels; 3 silk buttons. Both the cut and the length of this garment are characteristic urban Jewish men's wear in the early 20th century.
Woven wool, cotton, satin, 101 x 67 cm
Byelorussia, 1900-1920
from: unknown

7851-26
Matzah bag
A round matzah bag (Yiddish: matsa zeki) with three parts for keeping the matzes. The bag has chain-stitch embroidery showing a crown, and Hebrew text.
Cotton, silk, and woollen threads, 37 (diam.) cm
Byelorussia, 1900-1920
from: unknown

The synagogue of the Baal Shem Tov in Medzhibozh

Rabbi Baruch'l of Medzhibozh, the rabbi and the Be"sht's tefillin

Abraham Rechtman

There is an interesting story I feel I must include about an acrimonious dispute between Rabbi Baruch'l of Medzhibozh, the Be"sht's grandson, and Rabbi Shneur Zalman of Ladi, the Baal Hatania, which Chassidim maintain referred to the claim that the Be"sht's tefillin (phylacteries) were defective.

We heard the story in a home for the aged in Vinitze. I can still picture it: a group of old Jews sitting round a long table, An-sky talking pleasantly (as he always did) about the expedition and its aims, explaining how Baron Guenzburg, who was connected to the royal house, had contributed a fortune to save artifacts associated with Jewish life and how we were travelling across Ukraine on his instructions and at his expense. The old people listened and nodded, and so we gained their confidence and co-operation.

I remember one of these old Jews, a slim man, short and with a hunchback, wearing a short trimmed beard and a benign smile; almost playfully he told us the story about a remarkable meeting between these two rabbis. The old man told his story with such skill and imagination, in a flowery, educated Yiddish to which An-sky listened enraptured, hanging on to his every word. I tried to write down the story word for word, and to include the remarks made by the listeners who disliked the story-teller's obvious preference for Rabbi Shneur Zalman over Rabbi Baruch'l.

I regret that my prose cannot match the power of the old man's language, his use of idiom, intonation and especially the detailed, picturesque description of the great men's meeting in Rabbi Baruch's room and their terrifying dispute. What follows is an outline of the old man's story.

Rabbi Baruch of Medzhibozh was a very strict person, easily crossed and with a very quick temper. He was a proud man, for he was the Be"sht's grandson and prayed with his grandfather's tefillin. He considered himself unique, the best of his generation: so he respected no-one. There was only one chair in his 'special' room so that nobody could sit opposite him. He used to say: 'I was sent down to take charge of all the righteous.' And having assumed such a lofty role, as the old man said with a smile, it was hardly surprising that he was always angry and that he would explode at the drop of a hat. As we have already said, Rabbi Baruch distanced himself from everybody and kept aloof from the other righteous men and rabbis of his generation. Moreover, he had no respect for Rabbi Shneur Zalman of Ladi. This rabbi, a distinguished student of the Magid (preacher) of

Mezeritch, a great scholar who wrote his own Shulchan Aruch (a digest of Jewish laws), the author of the Baal Hatania. When Rabbi Shneur Zalman began to preach his system – Chabad – Rabbi Baruch'l dismissed it out of hand, refusing even to meet the rabbi.

It is well known, continued the old man, and both Chassidim and Jews versed in the ways of the world are well aware of the fact that Rabbi Shneur Zalman enjoyed a high reputation in royal circles. Governors and ministers treated him with respect, and through them he was able to learn in advance about the crown's plans for decrees against Jews.

Once Rabbi Shneur Zalman was informed by reliable sources that a decree was about to be issued forcing Jewish boys to be taken from their homes and enlisted in the army as soldiers. His sources told him that with a bribe it might still be possible to stop the enactment and cancel the decree.

The rabbi knew that without the support of Rabbi Baruch'l, one of the most influential people in Chassidic circles and some of whose followers were extremely rich men, he would be unable to collect such a large sum of money. So he sent a messenger to Rabbi Baruch'l with a sealed letter telling the great rabbi about the grave danger which threatened our nation's children. He asked him to help by collecting donations from his followers in order to counteract the decree. Rabbi Baruch'l answered Rabbi Shneur Zalman in a sealed letter entrusted into the hands of the messenger. He said that the heavens had not given him a sign that Jewish children would be conscripted into the army. This answer made Rabbi Shneur Zalman's Litvaker (Lithuanian) blood to boil; yet he realised that being angry would not help. So he sent then a second messenger to warn about the great danger that threatened. But Rabbi Baruch'l would not move an inch and repeated his answer. The heavens had not given him a sign that Jewish children would be conscripted into the army.

The old man, the story-teller, coughed as if Rabbi Baruch'l's answer had stuck in his throat. Some of the old people sitting round the table objected to the way in which he was belittling Rabbi Baruch'l and shouted 'stop', 'lies', 'he's talking nonsense' while he spoke. But that charming old man just smiled and carried on with his story as if they had meant someone else. Now, briefly, he examined their angry faces, smiled and continued.

Do you think, the old man asked, that Rabbi Shneur Zalman gave up and stopped bothering him? No, the

The synagogue of the Baal Shem Tov in Medzhibozh

Litvak was even more enraged with this haughty answer. He left everything behind him, took to the road and after a couple of days arrived in Medzhibozh to confront Rabbi Baruch'l.

Chassidim and Jews experienced in the ways of the world were present and all later described how Rabbi Shneur Zalman entered Rabbi Baruch'l's room, saluted the rabbi like a soldier and said: 'Rabbi Baruch, I must inform you that the crown is preparing an anti-Jewish decree according to which Jewish boys will be kidnapped and conscripted into the army. It is as clear as daylight that with a bribe we may still be able to cancel the decree. So, I come to you and ask your help in collecting the sum of money we need to cancel the decree.' Rabbi Baruch turned to the rabbi and answered stiffly: 'I have received no personal sign from the heavens that Jewish children are to be taken into the army.' The rabbi cut his salute abruptly. His hot Litvak blood began to boil and suddenly, with the force of a bullet, the rabbi let fly: 'Rabbi Baruch! You will surely pay for this. I warn you!' Rabbi Baruch leaped up from his chair and, standing face to face with the rabbi, he shouted in his ear: 'You impudent Litvak! Do you know who you are talking to? You are talking to Baruch, a grandson of the Be"sht z"l. I pray with my holy grandfather's tefillin!' But the rabbi was a Litvak through and through, and his blood began to boil even more; his anger flared up. The rabbi turned away from Rabbi Baruch, walked to the door, broke the handle off it and, throwing it on the floor, snapped at Rabbi Baruch: 'So what if the tefillin belonged to the Be"sht, does that mean they can't be defective?' And kicking the door open with his foot, he stormed out without another word.

Rabbi Baruch'l was dumb-struck. This was astonishing. He was panic-stricken. Defective tefillin? Had he been praying with defective tefillin? His head began to pound with pain and, as if he had been bitten by a snake, he shouted: 'Call Reb Hershl the scribe at once!' And when the scribe opened the tefillin they discovered that one letter in the text was indeed missing; one letter Yud was missing. Rabbi Baruch, felt as if he had been cut by a red-hot blade, he rose from his chair and in a strange, very different voice he cried out: 'What! the Litvak took a Yud from my tefillin? I shall take the letter Yud from his children!' [Yud is the first letter of the Hebrew word for children, Yeladim].

124

Alas, the rabbi's dour words – and here the old man sighed heavily – soon turned out to be true. One of Rabbi Shneur Zalman's children strayed from the straight and narrow. Some people even say that he changed religion, but this is pure fiction. After a short while he repented. But he used to torture himself in terrible ways: he used to tie his feet with a rope and hang upside down every night until dawn.

The old man had some other interesting anecdotes about Rabbi Shneur Zalman's visit to Medzhibozh. The morning after the meeting between the two rabbis, Rabbi Shneur Zalman decided to pay his tribute and visit the Be"sht's grave. But Rabbi Baruch'l gave orders to shut the cemetery gate and not to let him in. After a couple of days, a Jew from one of the nearby villages came to Rabbi Baruch and invited him to be the godfather at his son's circumcision. Rabbi Baruch'l told him that there was an important visitor in town and that he should also be invited to the feast. So naturally the Jew went to Rabbi Shneur Zalman and, total innocent that he was, said that Rabbi Baruch had asked him to invite the rabbi to the feast as well. The rabbi answered that if he would fetch Rabbi Baruch he would gladly join them. And so it was. The rabbi climbed into the carriage and sat beside Rabbi Baruch. They did not look at each other and neither uttered a word. As they were on their way Rabbi Shneur Zalman suddenly called the coachman and said: 'Turn to the right, there is a deep hole in the snow and, God forbid, we may overturn.' When he heard this, Rabbi Baruch'l remarked angrily: 'The Litvak wants to prove that he has studied the map. Well, we know the way here too!' The rabbi, his Litvak blood beginning to boil, reached out of the carriage, grabbed a handful of snow and turning to Rabbi Baruch'l he said: 'If you like I can show all four elements on your skin with this snow – fire, earth, wind and water.' Suddenly frightened, Rabbi Baruch'l caught his hand and shouted: 'No, no, there's no need.' Later, Rabbi Baruch'l commented that he had definitely seen the element 'fire'.

Index of objects

Acknowledgements

Exhibition

In Russia
Chief curator
Ludmila Uritskaya

Curators
N. Prokopieva
N. Cherunova

Translations Hebrew/Yiddish
M. Nosonovskii (Jewish University, St Petersburg)

Intermediary
Alla Geller, Holland Russia Trade Services

In the Netherlands
Exhibition curators
Judith C.E. Belinfante
Renée Waale

Coordinator
Bernadette van Woerkom

Translations
Sam Herman, Wendie Shaffer, Albertina Wijngaard

Design
BRS Premsela Vonk: Mieke Poot, Monique Rietberg

Technical realisation
Fa. Peeterse
Technische Dienst Joods Historisch Museum

Publicity
Agnes Duijves

Text coordinator
Mariëlla Beukers

Catalogue

Editors
Mariëlla Beukers & Renée Waale

Translation excerpts A. Rechtman
Shlomo Berger

Translations
Wendie Shaffer, Sam Herman

Photos
State Ethnographic Museum, St Petersburg
A. Ivanov
Anton Kras

Design
Roelof Koebrugge

Print
Waanders Printers, Zwolle

Published by
Waanders Publishers, Zwolle

© 1992 Uitgeverij Waanders b.v., Zwolle
State Ethnografic Museum, St Petersburg
Joods Historisch Museum, Amsterdam

CIP-gegevens Koninklijke Bibliotheek, Den Haag

Tracing

Tracing An-sky. - Zwolle : Waanders. - Ill.
Uitg. in samenw. met het Joods Historisch Museum,
Amsterdam
ISBN 90-6630-354-9
NUGI 641/639
Trefw.: Jodendom ; geschiedenis / Rusland ; folklore ;
geschiedenis.